MANUSCRIPT COLLECTIONS

OF

AFRICANA

IN
RHODES HOUSE LIBRARY
OXFORD

SUPPLEMENT

Compiled by

Louis B. Frewer

Superintendent of the Library

Bodleian Library
Oxford
1971

Printed by TRUEXpress Oxford

CONTENTS

INTRODUCTION

In 1968 there appeared <u>Manuscript Collections of Africana in Rhodes House Library, Oxford,</u> which listed about 1,250 items received to the end of 1967.

This volume has now been reprinted and it was thought to be an appropriate moment at which to issue a Supplement, the terminal date of which is 1970.

The format corresponds with that of the original publication: Rhodes House shelf-numbers have been added to entries for unrestricted material, but entries for collections still under an official or personal restriction bear no shelf-numbers and are further identified by an asterisk. Shelfmarks prefixed (B) indicate items held in the Department of Western Manuscripts at the Bodleian Library.

L. B. F.

AFRICA (in general)

1. ALL AFRICA CHURCH CONFERENCE. Report on church, youth and family; industrialisation and land; the church and citizenship; culture and religion; the growing church; message to the churches of Africa (1960). (Reprod. from typescript). MSS. Afr. s. 1324

2. *BARING (Evelyn, 1st Baron Howick of Glendale). Tape and transcript of interview: South Africa, Southern Rhodesia, High Commission Territories, Kenya, East African High Commission, 1929-59.

3. BEETON (William Hugh). Diary of a tour in Central and East Africa, Jan. 15 - Feb. 27, 1958, on behalf of Oversea Service. (Typescript). MSS. Afr. s. 1156

4. CAMPBELL (George B.). African witchdoctors, 1951-53; Survey plan of Kimberley mine, 1883 (photostat); British consulate, Zanzibar, 1900: photograph of members. MSS. Afr. s. 1393

5. DENNING (Alfred Thompson, Baron). Conference on the future of law in Africa, 1959-60, opening and introductory address, as Chairman, (with) text of speeches by delegates from Nigeria, Kenya, Tanganyika and Sudan. (Typescript). MSS. Afr. s. 1193

6. HUDSON (Rowland Skeffington). File of correspondence with Dr. J.H. Oldham mainly on Capricorn Africa Society matters, 1954-56. MSS. Afr. s. 1381

7. ——— Regional government and the provincial administration (in Africa), talk to Senior secretariat officers course, Colonial Office, 1957. (Typescript). MSS. Afr. s. 1395

8. JONES (Arthur Creech). Correspondence, records of visits to British dependencies, Labour Party's colonial policy, Colonial Development and Welfare, Secretary of State for the Colonies, &c., 1904-65. (Visits to Africa, boxes 12 and 13). MSS. Brit. Emp. s. 332

9. LANDRETH (G. J. T.). Typed diary of car journey from Cape Town to Nyasaland, Feb., 1954. MSS. Afr. s. 1371

10. *MORRIS (Barbara). Some journeys (in Africa and the Western Pacific), 1958-66. (Typescript, with 4 volumes of photographs).

11. WILBERFORCE (Samuel), successively Bishop of Oxford and of Winchester. Letters concerning the church in Central Africa, 1860-66; in South Africa, 1856-73. (B) MS. Wilberforce c. 19, ff. 1, 40

12. ——— Notes on the 'Colenso affair' (1853). (B) MS. Wilberforce c. 25, f. 102

13. ——— Letters to Robert Gray, Bishop of Cape Town, 1861-71. (B) MS. Wilberforce d. 39

ALGERIA

14. SINGER (Paul). Memorandum on land tenure in Algiers and Tunis,1919. (Type-script). MSS. Afr. s. 1252

CONGO

15. BROWNE (S. G.). Links with the past, as medical missionary, Yakusa, Belgian Congo (<u>c</u>. 1940). (Typescript). MSS. Afr. s. 1227

16. CHAPMAN (Everett G.) American Red Cross reports on Greek refugee camps, Belgian Congo, 1944, with photographs. (Typescript). MSS. Afr. r. 116(4)

17. GOWERS (Sir William Frederick). Correspondence, 1927-32, as Governor of Uganda; diary of a visit to the Belgian Congo, Apr. 18 - May 3, 1931; miscellaneous notes on African affairs, &c. 11 pts. (Mainly typescript). MSS. Afr. s. 1150

18. HALLAM (W. Keith R.). Typed letter to T. E. Letchworth regarding secondment of Nigerian personnel to police, Leopoldville, Congo, 1961. MSS. Afr. s. 1374

19. MIDDLETON (John Francis M.). Report on the Lugbara people of Uganda and Belgian Congo, with special reference to labour migration, 1951.(Typescript). MSS. Afr. s. 1220

20. *MORRIS (Barbara). Some journeys (in Africa and the Western Pacific), 1958-66. (Typescript, with 4 volumes of photographs).

ETHIOPIA & ERITREA

21. MACDONA (B. F.). Local leave, diary of a holiday in East Africa, 1936; The diary of an enemy, 1941, account of an official visit to Mogadiscio, Italian Somaliland, as banker; Ethiopian interlude, 1942; Kilimanjaro, 1944; East Africa in wartime, 1944; The bank in relation to post-war colonial development, 1943. 6 pts. (Xerox and typescript). MSS. Afr. s. 1312

22. MORLEY (John A. E.). Colonial service: letters to his Mother from Northern Nigeria, 1937-41; from Eritrea, 1941-44; from Singapore, 1945-47. With Chapters on Nigeria (in typescript). 2 vols. MSS. Brit. Emp. s. 27

23. PHILIPPS (James Erasmus T.). Abyssinia - Italian East Africa, notes made from observations, 1918-35, for Sir Miles Lampson, High Commissioner, Egypt and Sudan, to convey the current atmosphere, April 1935. (Typescript). MSS. Afr. s. 1170

24. TREVASKIS (Sir Gerald Kennedy N.). Correspondence, memoranda, &c., with British Military Administration in Eritrea, 1944-51; and as Political Officer and Agent in Western Aden, 1952-66. 6 boxes. MSS. Brit. Emp. s. 367

TUNISIA

25. SINGER (Paul). Memorandum on land tenure in Algiers and Tunis, 1919. (Type-script).   MSS. Afr. s. 1252

EAST AFRICA (in general, comprising four or more territories)

26. BREMNER (Bruce L.). Letters to his mother and sister from Nairobi as Loco-motive Superintendent on the Kenya railway, 1914-15, dealing mainly with the war in East Africa.   MSS. Afr. s. 1372

27. BRUTON (Charles Lamb). Joint select committee on East Africa (closer union), preliminary statement, with associated memoranda, correspondence, &c., 1930 -31; The Basoga; The Baganda; The Batwa; West Nile border disturbances, report, 1921; Letters from Africans, 1927-57 (Uganda). 6 files.   MSS. Afr. s. 1366(1-6)

28. COLLINS (R. L.). East African Customs and Excise Department (1890-1955). (Xerox).   MSS. Afr. s. 1161

29. CRABTREE (W. A.). Typed copy of journal of the 1892 missionary journey of Bishop Tucker's party from Mombasa to Kampala, with photographs.
                                                                                MSS. Afr. s. 1417(1)

30. EAST AFRICAN REFUGEE ADMINISTRATION. Formation; League of Poles in Africa; Polish repatriation mission, &c. Correspondence, memoranda, &c., 1942-47. C. L. Bruton, Commissioner. 11 files.   MSS. Afr. s. 1366(9)

31. ENGLEDOW (Sir Frank Leonard). Journals of agricultural tours: Mesopotamia, Nigeria, Trinidad, Malaya, West Indies, East Africa, 1918-57. 14 vols.
                                                                                MSS. Brit. Emp. s. 373

32. GETHIN (Richard). Diary, Jan. 17 - April 10, 1941: impressions while with the 1st South African Division and East African Military Labour Corps, 1941.
                                                                                MSS. Afr. s. 1277

33. HENN (Sir Sydney Herbert H.). Correspondence, memoranda, &c., of service with the Joint East Africa Board and of other activities in East Africa, 1922-36. 3 boxes.   MSS. Afr. s. 715

34. KIRK (C. C.). Correspondence with A. Creech Jones and others as Senior Assis-tant Accountant, Tanganyika railways, on sisal and alternative agricultural industries to avoid post war depression in East Africa, 1944-46. News cutting, the ground nut scheme, 1947. (Typescript).   MSS. Afr. s. 1184

35. MACDONA (B. F.). Local leave, diary of a holiday in East Africa, 1936; The diary of an enemy, 1941, account of an official visit to Mogadiscio, Italian Soma-liland, as banker; Ethiopian interlude, 1942; Kilimanjaro, 1944; East Africa in wartime, 1944; The bank in relation to post-war colonial development, 1943. 6 pts. (Xerox and typescript).   MSS. Afr. s. 1312

36. MATSON (A. T.). Wireless interception in the East African campaign, 1914-16, draft of an article. (Typescript). MSS. Afr. s. 1386, ff. 1-14

37. MEINHARD (H.). Typescript of lectures, 1-3, 5, 6, on the Bantu tribes of East Africa; material for lecture 4, c. 1945. Bibliography. 3 files. MSS. Afr. s. 1282

38. MONKHOUSE (Patrick). North of the Limpopo, c. 1951 (with) extracts from a note on the report of the East Africa Royal Commission. (Typescript).
MSS. Afr. s. 1239

39. NICKISSON (Rev.). From Mombasa to Mengo, being an account of the journey of 750 miles thro central Africa made by the missionary party under Bishop Tucker in 1892, with photographs & drawings, and tracings of original drawings.
MSS. Afr. s. 1417(2, 3)

40. OVERSEAS AUDIT SERVICE. A volume discovered in the Head Office in London containing letters, memoranda, press cuttings, &c. , illustrating in light vein the humour of auditors in East Africa, 1896-1946. MSS. Afr. r. 126

41. PADLEY (Wilfred). The needs for economic research and investigation in East Africa, c. 1954. (Typewritten). MSS. Afr. s. 1406

42. POLAK (Henry Salomon L.). Miscellaneous articles and correspondence on the Indian question in South and East Africa, 1906-44; Correspondence and memoranda on the Fiji sugar growers' dispute, 1943. (On loan). MSS. Brit. Emp. s. 372

43. SMITHEMAN (Frank). Letterbook as representative of Rhodesia Concessions in eastern Africa, 1897, 98. (On long loan). MSS. Afr. s. 1330(9)

44. WALKER (Charles William G.). Correspondence, minutes, agenda, &c. , as Secretary to the Conference of Governors of the East African Dependencies, 1925-35. 5 boxes. MSS. Afr. s. 717

45. WALTER (Albert). Echoes of a vanishing empire, being the memoirs of a meteorologist and civil servant in the Colonial empire (Mauritius and East Africa) from 1897 to 1947. 2 vols. (Typescript). MSS. Brit. Emp. r. 9, 10

46. WHITEHOUSE (B.). Account of the survey of the northern section of Lake Victoria, 1897-1910, as Surveyor, British East Africa; To the Victoria Nyanza by the Uganda railway, publ. 1902, in Journal of the Society of Arts; Positions, azimuths and lengths of sides of triangulation round the southern shores of Lake Victoria. MSS. Afr. s. 1294

———— Maps and charts (740.11 t. 1(26-50), 753.11 t. 1(21, 22), 752.11 t. 1(20-22)).

47. WILLIAMS (C. V.). Reports to the Council for technical education and training for overseas countries, East Africa, May 1963; Nigeria, Sept. 1963; Sierra Leone, Nov. 1963; Draft minutes of the 8th meeting of the Standing Committee, March 1964. 4 pts. (Reprod. from typescript). MSS. Afr. s. 1327(1-4)

KENYA

48. ARMSTRONG (Hon. Mrs. K.). Recollections of Kenya from 1919 to 1930.
     MSS. Afr. s. 1418

49. BEACH (Mervyn W. H.). Kikuyu system of land tenure, 1917. (Typescript).
     MSS. Afr. s. 1410

50. BEAUMONT (Ernest). Memoranda and correspondence as Director of Veterin-
     ary Services, Kenya, relating to the East African Veterinary Research Organis-
     ation, 1949-51; Report on the safety and efficacy of certain vaccines and on the
     conditions under which they are produced at the Kabete laboratory, by R. Daubney,
     1949. (Typescript).   MSS. Afr. s. 1344

51. BENHAM (R.). Drainage in the Rift Valley Province, Kenya, 1956; Internal
     drainage, South Kinangop scheme, 1963, as Senior Assistant Agricultural Officer;
     Settlement procedure as developed in Kenya, 1964 (with) diagram of settlement
     plots. (Typescript and xerox).   MSS. Afr. s. 1188

52. *BOOKLESS (I. P.). Palestine (police) and Kenya (forestry) diaries and papers,
     1941-55.

53. BREMNER (Bruce L.). Letters to his mother and sister from Nairobi as Loco-
     motive Superintendent on the Kenya railway, 1914-15, dealing mainly with the
     war in East Africa.   MSS. Afr. s. 1372

54. BROOKE-POPHAM (Sir Henry Robert M.). Personal papers, correspondence,
     &c., 1936-53, including period as Governor and C.-in-C., Kenya. 10 boxes.
     MSS. Afr. s. 1120

55. *BUXTON (Clarence Edward V.). Reports, memoranda, &c., of service in Kenya,
     c. 1919-61.

56. CAMERON (J. D.). National Farmers' Union, Kenya: minutes of meetings of
     Executive Committee, 1954. Tanganyika: Feb. 1955-Dec. 1966; Memorandum to
     the Water Legislation Committee (with) minutes of meeting, Nov. 1956. Misc.
     agricultural correspondence. (Typescript).   MSS. Afr. s. 1222

57. CARR (Herbert Alfred). Criminal case no. 1065 of 1950 (Mau Mau oaths) in Resi-
     dent Magistrate's Court, Naivasha, Kenya, as Ag. Resident Magistrate. (Type-
     script).   MSS. Afr. s. 1352

58. CHOLMONDELEY (Hugh, 3rd Baron Delamere). Letters to his wife from Kenya,
     Mar.-June 1930, Aug. 1931. (On long loan). With album of photographs taken by
     Lord Delamere during his expedition from Berbera to the Kenya Highlands in
     1896/97.   MSS. Afr. s. 1424

59. CLEAVER (Eric D.). Kenya constitutional conference, London: reception held at
     C. M. S. House, Jan. 22, 1960. (Xerox).   MSS. Afr. s. 1235

60. CLIVE (John Horace). Short history of Lamu, 1933, as District Officer, Kenya. (Typescript). MSS. Afr. s. 1273

61. COCHRAN (John M. C.). Ziwani irrigation scheme, Taveta district, Kenya, notes on work by 109 (E. A.) Construction Company, 1944–45; Notes on Mau Mau ceremonies as described by participants. (Mainly typescript).
MSS. Afr. s. 1271 a, b

62. *——— Memorandum on the Stamp Purchase Programme in Kenya, 1967. (Reprod. from typescript).

63. COOTE (John M.). Informal diary, Sept. 30, 1915–Dec. 10, 1917, as D. C., East Africa Protectorate; Typed copy of letter to Provincial Commissioner, Jinja, 1909, requesting extra medical assistance to combat the outbreak of plague at Mbale. MSS. Afr. r. 107

64. CORYNDON (Sir Robert Thorne). Correspondence, memoranda, &c., as Governor of Uganda, 1917-22; as Governor of Kenya, 1923-25; biographical material; Church Missionary Society correspondence, Kikuyu and land question, Kenya, 1903–47. 18 boxes. MSS. Afr. s. 633

65. DONALD (B. B.). Kenya reminiscences in the 1920's. (Typescript).
MSS. Afr. s. 1359

66. ELDAMA RAVINE. Diary of camps and Ravine diary, Kenya, 1894-1902. (Xerox of district record books). MSS. Afr. s. 1397

67. ELLIOT (John Augustus G.). Letters home, 1909-27, as A. D. C., Kenya; confidential correspondence and unofficial report on the Magadi railway, 1913; notes on Kericho District, 1913; correspondence (mainly copied) 1912–Sept. 1914; pocket diaries (fragmentary) 1914-18, 21-25. 12 pts. Photographs. MSS. Afr. s. 1179

68. FAZAN (Sidney H.). Miscellaneous notes on native laws and customs, Kenya, 1922-28, as D. C., Kenya; Native land trust ordinance, 1930; Report on the relations between government and local native councils, 1938; Memorandum regarding the draft native land tenure rules, 1956. 9 pts. Typescript. MSS. Afr. s. 1153

69. *——— Loyalist versus Mau Mau, a tribute to the tribal police, African guards and all loyalists of the Kikuyu, Embu and Meru tribes who resisted the Mau Mau revolt, 1956.

70. FITZGIBBON (Henry Elliot). Miscellaneous memoranda and correspondence relating to service in Kenya, 1928-34, as Municipal and Town Planning engineer; (incl.) An introduction to local government and town planning, 1933; Memorandum on the establishment of local government in Crown Colonies. 9 files & news cuttings. (Typescript). MSS. Afr. s. 1231

71. GALTON-FENZI (A. D.). Handing over report, Narok District, Kenya, March, 1957, as D. C. (Typescript). MSS. Afr. s. 1248

72. GETHIN (Richard). An old settler remembers, Kenya, 1908–58, draft MS. of autobiography; extracts publ. in Kenya Weekly News, 1955; correspondence with Editor of Kenya Weekly News, 1955; Diary, 1910, 1940–43; Diary, Jan. 17–April 10, 1941, impressions while with 1st South African Division and East African Military Labour Corps, 1941. 9 pts. (Mainly typescript).　MSS. Afr. s. 1277

73. HALE (G. M.). The Meru people take farewell of Dr. Hale: typed, signed letter of appreciation, Mar. 1, 1946 (with transl. into Engl.).　MSS. Afr. s. 1269

74. HARGREAVES (Anthony). The evolution of the Medical Training Centre, Nairobi, from 1951 to 62, with special reference to management. (Typescript).
MSS. Afr. s. 1307

75. HARLAND (R. D.). The revolution of tuberculous treatment amongst the Meru tribe of Kenya, as M. O. H., 1955–58 (with) appendices: value of exports, &c. (Typescript).　MSS. Afr. s. 1163

76. HARRIS (E. J. L.). A Community Development Officer's memories, Kenya, 1957 –65. (Typescript).　MSS. Afr. s. 1318

77. HAWKINS (E. B.). Tribes of the Rudolf province, Kenya, so far as is known in August, 1914. (Typescript).　MSS. Afr. s. 1408

78. *HECTOR (Gordon Matthews). Memoranda, notes, correspondence, &c., on military service in East Africa; as an administrator in Kenya, the Seychelles and in Basutoland as Leader of the House, 1940–67.

79. HOBBS (D.). Safari report, Gwassi Talai, 1961, as D. O., Kenya; handing over report, Kericho, Apr. 1962, Bomet division, Nov. 1962 (with) schedule of duties, Amboseli, 1963. (Mainly typescript).　MSS. Afr. s. 1190

80. HOLDING (E. Mary). The education of a Bantu tribe (the Meru of Kenya), 1958. (Typescript).　MSS. Afr. r. 117

81. HOLLIS (Sir Alfred Claud). The Wasegeju (their history and customs), 1899, as Assistant Collector, East Africa Protectorate. (Typescript with copy).
MSS. Afr. s. 1272 a, b

82. HOMAN (F. D.). Land tenure reform and agricultural development in the African lands of Kenya, by F. D. Homan and R. A. Sands, 1960. (Reprod. from typescript).
MSS. Afr. s. 1267

83. HUNTINGFORD (G. W. B.). A survey of the ancient and historical monuments and constructions in Nandi, 1927. (Reprod. from typescript).　MSS. Afr. s. 1396

84. JEANES SCHOOL. Correspondence, memoranda, circular letters, teacher's reports, courses, &c., Jeanes School, Kabete, Kenya, 1925–65. 2 files. (On loan).　MSS. Afr. s. 1367

85. KENYA. Provincial and district annual reports, 1904–62. In microfilm, 67 reels. (Kenya national archives).　Micr. Afr. 515

86. ———— Provincial and district record books, 1868-1952. In microfilm, 16 reels. (Kenya national archives).   Micr. Afr. 516

87. ———— Provincial and district handing over reports, 1913-61. In microfilm, 14 reels. (Kenya national archives).   Micr. Afr. 517

88. ———— Miscellaneous district correspondence, station diaries, tribal histories, ethnological papers, &c., 1901-62. In microfilm, 11 reels. (Kenya national archives).   Micr. Afr. 518

89. ———— Civil and military intelligence reports, by Administrative Officers, c. 1927-44. In microfilm, 12 reels. (Kenya national archives).   Micr. Afr. 519

90. KENYA Chief Secretary. Circulars issued from the Chief Secretary's office to all Government Departments and Ministries, 1921-62. In microfilm, 5 reels. (Kenya national archives).   Micr. Afr. 520

91. KENYA EUROPEAN AGRICULTURAL SETTLEMENT BOARD. Draft memorandum for the Royal Commission; Memoranda of the Kenya National Farmers' Union on Sessional paper no. 10 of 1958/59; Recommendations of the Board of Agriculture; correspondence, newscuttings. (Typescript).   MSS. Afr. s. 1195

92. KENYON (V. C. W.). Memorandum on land registration block plans and parcel numbers, 1957; on the transfer of land by gifts under Mohammedan law, Kenya, 1959. (Typescript).   MSS. Afr. s. 1251 a, b

93. KERIO. Notes on African customs taken from the Kerio provincial record book (1910). (Typescript).   MSS. Afr. s. 1415, ff. 1-11

94. KING (Anthony J.). Notes on the seismicity of the Lake Nyasa and Lake Rukwa areas, c. 1956. (Typescript).   MSS. Afr. s. 1281(2)

95. KNOWLES (E. J. F.). Budget survey of twenty Malindi (Kenya) fishermen, June-July 1951. (Typescript).   MSS. Afr. s. 1401

96. LAMBERT (Mrs. Roger Tuke). A political history of Baringo and Eldama Ravine districts, Kenya, 1947. (Xerox).   MSS. Afr. s. 1388

97. LEWIS (E. A.). Anthropological notes, Masai and kindred tribes, Kenya & Tanganyika (1930-46). (Typescript).   MSS. Afr. s. 1241

98. LIPSCOMB (J. F.). No signposts, the story of European agricultural settlement in Kenya, 1965. (Typescript).   MSS. Afr. r. 114

99. McKEAG (Victor Malcolm). Kenya, Meru district, annual report, 1944; handing over report, 1945; notes and correspondence on the M'Marete vs. Kirera civil case in the Supreme court, Nairobi, 1938. (Typescript).   MSS. Afr. s. 1189

100. MACNAGHTEN (Hilda). Happy days in East Africa, account of life in Kenya, 1906-1919, as the wife of a P. W. D. official; British Somaliland, land of sunshine, 1920-32. (Typescript).   MSS. Afr. s. 1217

101. MARTIN (Walter). Friends Service Council. Friends visit to Jomo Kenyatta at Maralal, Kenya, June 1961. (Xerox). MSS. Afr. s. 1236

102. MERU METHODIST MISSION. Correspondence dealing with the education of the tribe, Kenya: literacy, adult education, administration, orthography, 1937-56. 6 files. MSS. Afr. s. 1380

103. *MILLER (J.). Papers relating to the Kenya African Union, 1952-55.

104. MITFORD-BARBERTON (Raymond B.). In quest of the Loonburg duiker, and other papers on life in Kenya, 1926-34; correspondence, mainly on early settlers, with the Kenya History Society, 1954-57. (Mainly typescript). News cuttings. MSS. Afr. s. 1166

105. MOUSLEY (J. C. A.). Report on visit to Nairobi by the Senior Principal (Training), Ministry of Transport and Works, Mar. 1965, with Summary of recommendations and conclusions. (Typescript). MSS. Afr. s. 1399

106. *NAIROBI CHAMBER OF COMMERCE. Minute books, 1909-63.

107. NANDI RISING. Papers connected with attempted Nandi rising, Kenya, 1923. (In typescript). MSS. Afr. s. 1353

108. OSBORNE (George Harold). The Wadigo of Vanga District (c. 1920) as D. C., East Africa Protectorate. (Typescript, with copy). MSS. Afr. s. 1253

109. *PADLEY (Wilfred). File of notes on financial matters between W. Padley as Minister of Finance and a number of Kenya individuals, 1946.

110. PITT (Mrs. C. J.). Who killed Lord Erroll? Kenya, 1941, unpublished story of events leading up to Sir Delver Broughton's trial for murder and acquittal, as Secretary to the Prosecutor. (Typescript). MSS. Afr. s. 1345

111. PITT (Charles Sydney). Annual reports, Embu district, Kenya, medical and sanitary services, 1947, 48, 49, as M. O.; Eldoret native civil hospital, 1951, 52, 55. (Typescript). MSS. Afr. s. 1194

112. ——— Malaria control and its relation to other environmental work in a European settled area, Kenya colony. Diss., D. P. H. course, 1955. MSS. Afr. r. 104

113. POWLES (Stephen Howard). Estate manager's diary, Kenya, 1928-54. 6 vols. MSS. Afr. s. 1121

114. *RENISON (Sir Patrick). Papers: Trinidad and Tobago, British Honduras, British Guiana, Kenya, 1949-62.

115. RICE (R. K.). File of correspondence, Mombasa W/T station, 1914-15, including intercepted messages, &c., with draft of an article by A. T. Matson, Wireless interception in the East African campaign, 1914-16. (Typescript). MSS. Afr. s. 1386

116. *ROGERS (Sir Philip). Tape and transcript of interview: service in Nigeria, Kenya, &c., 1947-63.

117. ROSS (William McGregor). Kenya: P.W.D. reports, 1905/6 - 1924; Report on the Tana river, 1909; draft MS. of <u>Kenya from within</u>, publ. 1927; misc. official and private correspondence, news cuttings, maps, photographs, &c., 1900-35. 5 vols. MSS. Afr. s. 1178

118. SANDS (R.A.). Land tenure reform and agricultural development in the African lands of Kenya, by F.D. Homan and R.A. Sands, 1960. (Reprod. from typescript). MSS. Afr. s. 1267

119. *SCOTT (Sir Robert). Personal correspondence: Uganda, Kenya, Gold Coast, Palestine, Mauritius, 1928-58.

120. SOUTH KAVIRONDO. Petition, signed, from Chiefs and Elders, listing requests for submission to visiting Members of Parliament, 1944. MSS. Afr. s. 424, f. 535

121. SOUTHERN MASAI RESERVE. Typed copy of Southern Masai reserve district political record book from the commencement to the 31st December 1911. MSS. Afr. s. 1409

122. SPELLER (Charles). A review of the native policy of Kenya colony; Memorandum submitted to the Joint parliamentary committee upon closer union in the East African territories, 1931. (Typescript). MSS. Afr. s. 1178(4), ff. 336-409

123. SUTTON (H.M.A.). Handing over notes, Marsabit, Kenya, Dec. 27, 1950, as Grazing Control Officer. (Typescript). MSS. Afr. s. 1326

124. TALBOT-SMITH (L.). Historical record of Tanaland, 1921, as D.C., Lamu, Kenya. (Typescript). MSS. Afr. s. 1274

125. THOMPSON (Frederick T.). Correspondence, articles, memoranda, &c., as a member of the United Country Party in Kenya and of the Nairobi City Council, 1952-61. 5 files. MSS. Afr. s. 908

126. TREMBETH (Rosalie). Newsletters, 1937-43, as Salvation Army officer in charge of a school and welfare centre, Kenya; The making of a mountaineer, account of a journey to Kilimanjaro, 1941. (Typescript). Newscuttings. MSS. Afr. s. 1154

127. TURBO-KIPKARREN ASSOCIATION. Correspondence, reports, minute books, and memoranda, 1928-63. MSS. Afr. s. 881

128. *TURNBULL (Sir Richard). Tape and transcript of interview: colonial administrative service, Kenya, 1931-58.

129. *WALKER (P.H.). Miscellaneous administrative reports, &c., Kenya and Aden, 1950-60.

130. WATKINS (O.F.). Tribal laws and customs, Kenya: Elgayo, Kamasia, Marakwet, Nandi, Turkana, Use in Gishu Masai, Wanderobo (1920). 8 pts. (Typescript). MSS. Afr. s. 1394

FEDERATION OF RHODESIA & NYASALAND

131. HODGSON (R. G.). Reports to the Council for technical education and training for overseas countries, Central Africa (N. Rhodesia, Nyasaland, S. Rhodesia), Oct. 1963; Republic of the Sudan, Feb. 1964. (Reprod. from typescript).

MSS. Afr. s. 1327 (5,6)

132. *HONE (Sir Ralph). Personal papers relative to the preparation of a constitution for a projected independent federal republic of East Africa, 1963/64.

133. JENKINS (Sir Edward Enoch). Judgments on cases in the Rhodesia and Nyasaland Court of Appeal, 1949-54; Speeches on the occasion of the retirement of Sir Robert Hudson, Chief Justice, Southern Rhodesia, May 15, 1950. (Typescript).

MSS. Afr. s. 1244

134. *KENNEDY (Sir John Noble). The birth of the Central African Federation, 1966. (Typescript).

135. MONCKTON REPORT. Summary of the main findings and recommendations... of the Advisory commission on the review of the constitution of the Federation of Rhodesia and Nyasaland, 1960. (Typescript).   MSS. Afr. s. 1200, ff. 1-13

136. NYASALAND EDUCATION DEPARTMENT. Circulars: courses, bursaries, scholarships, &c., 1957-61 (with similar papers for Rhodesia and Nyasaland, 1958-59). (Reprod. from typescript).   MSS. Afr. s. 1319

137. NYASALAND NATIONAL CONGRESS. Why we oppose federation, our aims and objects. Statement from Nyasaland Africans to the British Government, Members of Parliament and people, Jan. 1, 1952. (Typescript).   MSS. Afr. s. 1321

NYASALAND/MALAWI

138. BAYLISS (R. M.). Ulendo notes, travelling diary as Administrative officer, Fort Johnston, Nyasaland, 1956-63.   MSS. Afr. s. 1382

139. BURKINSHAW (P. L.). Nyasaland: Kasupe district annual report, 1960; Handing over notes, Kasupe, Chikwawa districts, 1961, 63; Government agents, duties, 1963. 4 pts. (Typescript).   MSS. Afr. s. 1407(3)

140. *DEVLIN (Patrick Arthur, Baron). Nyasaland Commission of Inquiry, 1959: evidence, memoranda, drafts, &c.

141. DICKSON (A. G.). An experiment in mass education, Nyasaland and Northern Rhodesia tour of the East Africa Command mobile propaganda unit, 1944, report.

MSS. Afr. s. 1159

142. *GANDY (Maurice N.). Appreciation of the situation (Nyasaland), April 1959; On a realistic policy in Nyasaland, Sept. 1959, as D. C., Lilongwe; Correspondence,

Feb. – Oct. 1959, mainly with J. H. Ingham, Secretary of African Affairs. (Typescript).

143. GARNETT (C. B.). The Kota Kota Rice Society, I td. , Nyasaland, 1946, memorandum. MSS. Afr. s. 1199(1)

144. JONES (Griff Bevan). Touring diaries, as Administrative Officer, Nyasaland, 1951/52 and 1952/53. 2 vols. MSS. Afr. r. 123, 124

145. MACMILLAN (Maurice Harold). Address at a civic luncheon at Blantyre, Jan. 26, 1960, as Prime Minister, Great Britain. (Typescript). MSS. Afr. s. 1265

146. NORMAN (L. S.). Rebellion, a report of the native rising, Nyasaland. Jan. 1915. (Typescript). MSS. Afr. s. 1160

147. NYASALAND. Record of a meeting between the Governor and Ralph Chinyama, President-General of the Nyasaland African Congress, 1952; Why federation? 1952; circular letters to civil servants from Prime Minister Hastings Banda, 1963, 64. Local newspapers, 1962-66. MSS. Afr. s. 1177

148. NYASALAND EDUCATION DEPARTMENT. Circulars: courses, bursaries, scholarships, &c. , 1957-61 (with similar papers for Rhodesia and Nyasaland, 1958, 59). (Reprod. from typescript). MSS. Afr. s. 1319

149. NYASALAND NATIONAL CONGRESS. Why we oppose federation, our aims and objects. Statement from Nyasaland Africans to the British Government, Members of Parliament and people, Jan. 1, 1952. (Typescript). MSS. Afr. s. 1321

150. POPPER (Eric Otto). Miscellaneous notes and reports on the Kota Kota Produce and Trading Society, Ltd. , Nyasaland, as Managing Director; minutes of meetings 1960, 61; Inspector's report to the Financial Secretary, 1961; balance sheets, 1958-61. (Typescript). MSS. Afr. s. 1199(2)

151. ROBINS (J. W.). Miscellaneous reports and memoranda on tribal organisation, the development of local government, district councils, etc. , 1949-61, as Local Government Officer, Nyasaland; papers for discussion at Provincial Commissioners' conference, 1958. (Typescript). MSS. Afr. s. 1211

152. SHARPE (Alfred). Copies of correspondence upon administrative matters from Vice Consulate, Blantyre, Nyasaland, 12th Aug. –8th Sept. 1893. Treasury circular, no. 31 of 1912. Directive to police and army officers, 1953. MSS. Afr. s. 1202

153. STEELE (B.). Reports on the Karonga reclamation scheme, Nyasaland, 1955-57, as tsetse botanist; Annual report, 1959, Lower Shire veterinary department; Emergency diary, Central Province, Feb. , March 1959; Notes for overseas officers; Citumbuka lessons. (Typescript). MSS. Afr. s. 1264

154. THOMSON (Thomas Davidson). Draft annual report, 1939, Upper Shire District, Nyasaland, as Assistant D. O. , notes on the Chiefs and Chiefdoms; Educating the East African soldier, 1942; report on African demobilization, Dec. 1945, Aug. 1946; miscellaneous reports: Domasi Community Development Scheme, African adult education, &c. , 1956-60. 2 files. (Typescript). MSS. Afr. s. 1158

155. WAGNER (M.S.). Report by the D.C., Luanshya, on a visit to Lusaka, Zomba, Blantyre and Bulawayo with officials of Roan Antelope Copper Mines Ltd. of Luanshya, 1961. (Typescript). MSS. Afr. s. 1360

RHODESIA (Northern)/ZAMBIA

156. AKEROYD (A.). Northern Rhodesia, report of visit to Fort Jameson division, 1948, as Assistant Architect. (Typescript). MSS. Afr. s. 1185

157. BENSON (Sir Arthur Edward T.). Statement broadcast by... the Governor of Northern Rhodesia, on Mar. 12, 1959 (state of emergency). (Reprod. from typescript). MSS. Afr. s. 1400

158. *BILLING (Melvin George). Notes on six provincial tours of inspection in Northern Rhodesia, 1959-60.

159. BIRKS (D.T.M.). Xerox copies of two memoranda, as A.D.C., Gombe division, N. Rhodesia, on the proposed reorganisation of the Waja native authority, Aug., Sept. 1945, with covering letter. MSS. Afr. s. 1024

160. BOWN (J.H.F.). Reports of two district tours, April, May, 1959, as D.O., Northern Rhodesia. MSS. Afr. s. 1201

161. BUTTON (E.L.). Annual report on African affairs, North-Western province, Northern Rhodesia, 1960. (Reprod. from typescript). MSS. Afr. s. 1422

162. BWALYA (Stephen). Customs and habits of the Bemba (1936). (Xerox).
MSS. Afr. s. 1214

163. CHAPMAN (Allan Simpson). Records of cases in the Court of the Magistrate, Ndola, as D.O. for the Luangwa district of Northern Rhodesia, Nov.-Dec., 1929. (Typescript). MSS. Afr. s. 1216

164. COTTRELL (J.A.). Letter to G. Stokes, Resident Magistrate, Mongu, regarding the Barotse National School, 1935. (Typescript). MSS. Afr. s. 1347(2)

165. COVERDALE (G.M.). Natural Resources Development College, Zambia: reports and minutes of the first six meetings, 1964-65; Recruiting for Zambia in the United Kingdom, 1965; College curricula, Feb. 1966. 3 pts. (Typescript).
MSS. Afr. s. 1176

166. DEAN (J.E.H.). Miscellaneous notes, Kasama station, Northern Rhodesia; incl. census of Europeans, 1902; origin of the Wawemba; statement made by Chief Chikwanda, 1936; fishing developments on Lake Tanganyika. (Typescript, xerox).
MSS. Afr. s. 1212

167. DENNY (Spencer Reeve). Up and down the great north road (life in Northern Rhodesia, 1932-46). (Typescript, 1970). MSS. Afr. r. 113

168. DICKSON (A. G.). An experiment in mass education, Nyasaland and Northern Rhodesia tour of the East Africa Command mobile propaganda unit, 1944, report.

MSS. Afr. s. 1159

169. FLEMING (C. J. Wallace). Elements of customary law in the Lundazi district, Northern Rhodesia, 1964 (unpubl. dissertation), as Admin. Officer (with) criticisms by Sir George Paterson, as Chief Justice, Northern Rhodesia, and others. (Type-script).

MSS. Afr. s. 1243

170. *GARDNER (T. C.). Tapes and transcript of interview, 1969: service in Northern Rhodesia, 1946-64, latterly as Minister of Finance.

171. GUILBRIDE (Patrick D. L.). Pawpaw picnic (veterinary service in Northern Rhodesia), n. d. (Typescript, on long loan).

MSS. Afr. s. 1315

172. GUINNESS (Walter Edward, 1st Baron Moyne). Despatch to the Officer administering the Government of Northern Rhodesia, April 1941, on future land policy; reply from the Acting Governor; prospects for Afrikaners in Northern Rhodesia, 1949; miscellaneous typescript and news cuttings on current affairs. (Type-script).

MSS. Afr. s. 1192

173. HANNAH (John William). Evidence before a commission of enquiry, Chinsali district, Northern Rhodesia, into disturbances between Alice Lenshina, her dea-cons and supporters, and the U. N. I. P. , June-July, 1964, as D. C. , Chinsali. (Xerox).

MSS. Afr. s. 1363

174. HART (Rupert L. L.). Diary as Veterinary Officer, Northern Rhodesia, 1910-12. (On long loan).

MSS. Afr. r. 112

175. HEATHCOTE (G. C. M.). Northern Rhodesia administration: Northern Province newsletter; Notes on Kalabo, Mankoya, Senanga, Mongu districts; on Barotseland protectorate, newsletter; Secretariat newsletters, 1954-60. (Typescript).

MSS. Afr. s. 1387

176. HOWE (R. A.). Recollections of police service, Northern Rhodesia, from 1911.

MSS. Afr. s. 424, ff. 531-534

177. *HUDSON (Rowland Skeffington). Tapes and transcript of record of service in Northern Rhodesia, the Colonial Office African Studies Branch, Northern Nigeria, Ministry of Overseas Development, 1919-66.

178. *——— Future relations between H. M. Government and Barotseland, 1962. (Reprod. from typescript).

179. JOHNSTON (Russell R.). American Red Cross reports on Polish refugee camps in Tanganyika, Northern and Southern Rhodesia, 1944. 3 vols. , with photographs. (Typescript).

MSS. Afr. r. 116

180. LAWRANCE (John G.). Miscellaneous memoranda and reports on community and social development, Northern Rhodesia, 1952-63, as D. O. (incl.) annual reports of Namushakende development area, 1952-55. (Typescript). (On long loan).

MSS. Afr. s. 1180

181. LOCAL GOVERNMENT SERVICE COMMISSION. Report, 1964 (with) schedule
      of salary scales. (Typescript).   MSS. Afr. s. 1200, ff. 14-95

182. *MACKINTOSH (I. R.). Chingola, Northern Rhodesia: memorandum, diary,
      police reports, &c., of riots, 1963 (with) District Commissioner's monthly intel-
      ligence reports, 1962-64.

183. MHELENGE. Typed extracts from Mhelenge district notebook, 1899-1922,
      collected by J. Fowlie.   MSS. Afr. s. 1355

184. MIDDLETON (P. C.). The Senanga district (Northern Rhodesia), a survey, 1956.
      (Typescript).   MSS. Afr. s. 1411

185. MILLAR-SMITH (Richard). The unveiling of a monument marking the site of the
      surrender of General von Lettow Vorbeck, 1918, on the bank of Chambeshi river,
      Northern Rhodesia; historical notes of the Babemba tribe, compiled by P. C. Cook-
      son, R. Young and R. Millar-Smith, from notes made by White Fathers, 1902-54.
      (Typescript).   MSS. Afr. s. 1213(1, 2)

186. STUART (I. MacN.). Report on the death and funeral of the Mulena Mukwae
      Mulima Nalolo, Feb. 27, 1959, as D. C., Barotseland, Northern Rhodesia. (Type-
      script).   MSS. Afr. s. 1254(1)

187. THOM (Andrew). European education in Northern Rhodesia (a student's essay),
      c. 1962; Monthly bulletin of the Kabwe arts society (co-operative) limited, Aug.,
      1968. (Typescript, on loan).   MSS. Afr. s. 1314(1, 2)

188. THOMSON (H. H.). Memorandum on the policy and structure of local govern-
      ment in the rural areas of Northern Rhodesia, 1960. (Typescript). (On loan).
                                                           MSS. Afr. s. 1254(2)

189. WAGNER (M. S.). Report by the D. C., Luanshya, on a visit to Lusaka, Zomba,
      Blantyre and Bulawayo with officials of Roan Antelope Copper Mines Ltd. of
      Luanshya, 1961. (Typescript).   MSS. Afr. s. 1360

190. WIENAND (Carlie E.). Reminiscences (Northern Rhodesia, 1874-1906, incl.
      account of Cecil Rhodes's funeral), typescript of tape recording made at Broken
      Hill; Reminiscences of the last of the Zeederbergers, coaching days, 1896-97.
      (Typescript, on loan).   MSS. Afr. s. 1314(3, 4)

191. *WILMOT (A. T. de B.). Reports, correspondence, despatches, Secretariat and
      Ministerial minutes: Northern Rhodesia, Gold Coast, Colonial Development Cor-
      poration, c. 1930-60. (On loan).

192. WILSON (G. H.). Citations for awards and decorations for African soldiers of the
      Northern Rhodesia Regiment for service in Somaliland, 1940. (Xerox copy).
                                                           MSS. Afr. s. 1171

193. WRIGHT (D. M.). National Food and Nutrition Commission, outline of nutrition work
      in Northern Rhodesia, post-1960 (reprod. from typescript); sundry papers on iron
      smelting in Northern Rhodesia, 1926-60. (Typewritten).   MSS. Afr. s. 1420

RHODESIA (Southern)/RHODESIA

194. BOSAZZA (V. L.). Notes on the Journal of Thomas Baines made during his expedition up the Zambesi river with Dr. Livingstone, 1858. (Xerox of typescript, 1970).   MSS. Afr. s. 424, ff. 546-556

195. HART (Rupert L. L.). Notes (on the history of veterinary development in Southern Rhodesia, 1954). (Typescript).   MSS. Afr. s. 1390

196. JENKINS (Sir Edward Enoch). Judgments on cases in the Rhodesia and Nyasaland Court of Appeal, 1949-54; Speeches on the occasion of the retirement of Sir Robert Hudson, Chief Justice, Southern Rhodesia, May 15, 1950. (Typescript).
MSS. Afr. s. 1244

197. JOHNSTON (Russell R.). American Red Cross reports on Polish refugee camps in Tanganyika, Northern and Southern Rhodesia, 1944, 3 vols., with photographs. (Typescript).   MSS. Afr. r. 116

198. MORRIS (Guy W.). The making of Rhodesia (submitted for the Beit Prize, Oxford, 1910). (Typewritten).   MSS. Afr. r. 103

199. NEWNHAM (F. J.). To the Victoria Falls of the Zambesi, by a vagrant (F. J. Newnham), 1895. (Xerox).   MSS. Afr. r. 115

200. PATEMAN (Trevor John). African agriculture and European settlement, the political economy of land in Rhodesia, 1968. (Xerox).   MSS. Afr. s. 1423

201. SMITHEMAN (Frank). Letterbook as representative of Rhodesia Concessions in eastern Africa, 1897, 98. (On long loan).   MSS. Afr. s. 1330(9)

202. STANLEY (Sir Herbert James). Correspondence, 1910-41, and memoranda (incl.) report of an informal discussion with General Smuts, 1910; the constitutional question in Southern Rhodesia (c. 1920), as Imperial Secretary, South Africa; on the Bledisloe report (c. 1937), as Governor, Southern Rhodesia. (Mainly typescript).   MSS. Afr. s. 1250

203. WAGNER (M. S.). Report by the D. C., Luanshya, on a visit to Lusaka, Zomba, Blantyre and Bulawayo with officials of the Roan Antelope Copper Mines Ltd. of Luanshya, 1961. (Typescript).   MSS. Afr. s. 1360

SOMALILAND

204. ELLISON (Randall Erskine). Tapes and transcript of interview: education service in Northern Nigeria, Somaliland and Tanganyika, 1928-57. (Typescript).
MSS. Afr. s. 1332

205. HUNT (John Anthony). Correspondence with the Governor and Chief Secretaries of Somaliland regarding the General Survey, 1938-51; papers and maps relating

to meteorological and tribal movement data, 1946–50; tribal genealogical notes, 1945–46. 6 pts. MSS. Afr. s. 1365

206. MACDONA (B. F.). Local leave, diary of a holiday in East Africa, 1936; The diary of an enemy, 1941, account of an offical visit to Mogadiscio, Italian Somaliland, as banker; Ethiopian interlude, 1942; Kilimanjaro, 1944; East Africa in wartime, 1944; The bank in relation to post-war colonial development, 1943. 6 pts. (Xerox and typescript). MSS. Afr. s. 1312

207. MACNAGHTON (Hilda). Happy days in East Africa, account of life in Kenya, 1906 –1919, as wife of P. W. D. official; British Somaliland, land of sunshine, 1920–32. (Typescript). MSS. Afr. s. 1217

208. WILSON (G. H.). Citations for awards and decorations for African soldiers of the Northern Rhodesia Regiment for service in Somaliland, 1940. (Xerox copy). MSS. Afr. s. 1171

SUDAN & BRITISH ADMINISTRATION IN EGYPT

209. *BELL (Sir Gawain). Tape and transcript of interview: service in the Sudan and Northern Nigeria, &c. , 1931–62.

210. HODGSON (R. G.). Reports to the Council for technical education and training for overseas countries, Central Africa (N. Rhodesia, Nyasaland, S. Rhodesia), Oct. 1963; Republic of the Sudan, Feb. 1964. (Reprod. from typescript). MSS. Afr. s. 1327(5, 6)

211. *MacMICHAEL (Sir Harold). Files of correspondence and papers relating to his service in the Sudan, Tanganyika, Palestine, Malaya, Malta, &c. , 1905–46.

212. PHILIPPS (James Erasmus T.). Abyssinia-Italian East Africa, notes made from observations, 1918–35, for Sir Miles Lampson, High Commissioner, Egypt and Sudan, to convey the current atmosphere, April 1935. (Typescript). MSS. Afr. s. 1170

TANGANYIKA/TANZANIA

213. *ALLSEBROOK (Geoffrey P.). File of documents relating to service in Tanganyika and the British Virgin Islands, 1946–61, including a report upon the deposition of Chief Raphael Njahite, Ulanga district, 1960.

214. ARRIGONE (J. L.). Progress report (on house building) prepared for the Government of Tanzania under the United Nations development programme, 1966. Photographs. (Typescript). MSS. Afr. r. 109

215. BARTON (D.). Tanganyika: annual reports, Masasi district, 1957; Ukerewe

district, 1958–60; Final financial statement, Masasi local treasury, 1957, as D. C., Tanganyika; A note on the judicial system; Some problems in local government; draft Handbook for Councillors; fragmentary diary, 1952–60.

MSS. Afr. s. 1230

216. *——— Draft of letter to Julius Nyerere upon resignation from the Colonial Service, Tanganyika, 1961. (On long loan).

217. BLANCHE (R. B.). Tanganyika. Report on the operation of the contractor finance scheme by the Ministry of Communications and Works, 1964; Suggestion for the improvement of the efficiency & effectiveness of the Exchequer and Audit Department, 1967. (Typescript). MSS. Afr. s. 1356(1, 2)

218. BURTT (B. D.). Draft copy of "An enumeration of the principal vegetation types found in the Central and Lake Province of Tanganyika territory and associated with the tsetse fly problem", 1936; Some observations on the natural thickets near old Shinyanga, 1932. (Typescript). MSS. Afr. s. 1263 (1, 2)

219. CAMERON (J. D.). National Farmers' Union, Kenya: minutes of meetings of Executive Committee, 1954. Tanganyika: Feb. 1955 – Dec. 1966; Memorandum to the Water Legislation Committee (with) minutes of meeting, Nov. 1966. Misc. agricultural correspondence. (Typescript). MSS. Afr. s. 1222

220. CIVIL SERVICE TRAINING CENTRE. Notes for students of the Instructor course, Dar es Salaam, 1964. (Typescript). MSS. Afr. s. 1228

221. CONNELLY (D.). Memorandum on local authority finance, Bukoba, Tanganyika (1906); Amendments to Nyarubanja rules; Some notes on Buhaya council's draft estimates for 1962. (Typescript). (On loan). MSS. Afr. s. 1416

222. *——— District Officer's court judgments, Bukoba, Tanganyika, 1960–62. 2 files. (On loan).

223. CORY (H.). The people of the Lake Victoria region, 1950, address to members of Lake Province Society. (Typescript). MSS. Afr. s. 1261

224. DAVIES (Vera M.). Zanzibar Welfare Office, miscellaneous papers, 1954–59; African budget survey, Dar es Salaam, Tanganyika, 1956/57. MSS. Afr. s. 1317

225. DAWSON (L. K.). Kilimanjaro native authority forest reserve, annual report, 1947, 48, with other reports on forest stations in Tanganyika, 1947–65. (Xerox).

MSS. Afr. s. 1364

226. DOWSETT (Francis Dudley). Letters home, 1931–64, as Administrative Officer, Tanganyika (with) Airgraph letters, 1942–44. MSS. Afr. s. 1276

227. ELLISON (Randall Erskine). Tapes and transcript of interview: education service in Northern Nigeria, Somaliland and Tanganyika, 1928–57. (Typescript).

MSS. Afr. s. 1332

228. ENGLISH (M. J. W.). Reconnaissance survey of Missouri Plantations Limited,

Arusha, 1962, as Agricultural officer, Tanganyika; Reorganisation of the Tanganyika Agricultural Corporation settlement schemes in the Kilombero valley, 1964; Proposals for the establishment of a settlement scheme at Kiwanda in Tanga region, 1966. Plans. 3 files. (Typescript).   MSS. Afr. s. 1295

229. *FLETCHER-COOKE (Sir John). Tapes and transcript of interview: service in Colonial Office, Malaya, Tanganyika, 1934-61.

230. FOX (R. F.). Report on investigations into and proposals for the solution of the squatter problem on certain estates in the Amani area, Tanganyika, 1959. (Typescript).   MSS. Afr. s. 1164

231. GILLMAN (Clement). Tanganyika diaries, 1905-43 (with) letters and news cuttings, as railway engineer: 1905-14 (1906-13 in German) for German colonial administration; 1916-37 for British; as water consultant, 1938-40; Geographical notes, 2 vols., photographic negatives. 22 vols. (Mainly typescript).
MSS. Afr. s. 1175

232. GRANT (H. St. John). Masai history and mode of life, a summary, prepared for the Committee of enquiry into the Serengeti National Park, 1957, as D. O., Tanganyika; Memorandum by the Masai of the National Park, 1957. (Typescript).
MSS. Afr. s. 1237

233. GRANTHAM (Donald R.). Correspondence, memoranda, &c., as Acting Chief Inspector of Mines, Tanganyika, with diaries (23 vols.), and albums of photographs (10 vols.), 1926-47, including a visit to British Guiana in 1933-34.
MSS. Brit. Emp. s. 374

234. GROOME (J. S.). History of the Forest Department, Tanganyika (1921-50). (Typescript).   MSS. Afr. s. 1389

235. HALL (C. L.). The influence of the social system and environment on the health of a primitive people, a study of the Masai tribe in Tanganyika; dissertation for the diploma in public health, London University, 1956. (Typescript).
MSS. Afr. s. 1183

236. HANDLEY (J. R. F.). Banded ironstones and associated rocks, 1956, report no. JRFH/50, Geological Survey of Tanganyika. (Typescript).   MSS. Afr. s. 1281(4)

237. HARRIS (C. C.). Tanganyika, notes and reports as D. C., 1951-58; policy and organisation of the Public Relations Dept., as Director of Public Relations, 1958-59; memorandum and reports as P. C., 1960-62. News cuttings, (Typescript).   MSS. Afr. s. 1157

238. HEATH (Douglas Frank). African secret societies (Nigeria); Circulars, articles, memoranda, &c., as D. O., Nigeria and in Medical Department, Tanganyika, 1920-62; Election as European Member of the Legislative Council, Tanganyika, 1959; Photographs. 5 vols.   MSS. Afr. s. 1342

239. HOCKIN (V. T.). Mines division, Tanganyika: extracts from annual reports, 1922-25; Review of the mining industry, 1958, 59, 62, 63; Brief history of mining in Tanganyika; Notes on Tanganyika Government's interest in mining concerns; Procedure for the export of diamonds; photographs, news cuttings. (Typescript).
MSS. Afr. s. 1281(1)

240. *HOLMES-SIEDLE (Rt. Rev. J.), Bp. of Kigoma. Tape and transcript of discussion with J. J. Tawney concerning British administration, missions, native customs, education and conditions before and since independence in Tanzania, 1946-69.

241. ISHERWOOD (Albert Arthur M.). Memoranda, as Director of Education, Tanganyika, on Nyakato school and the question of re-opening a government central school in Bukoba district, 1939. (Typewritten).   MSS. Afr. s. 999(2), ff. 160-172

242. JAMES (T. C.). The nature of rift faulting in Tanganyika, c. 1956. (Typescript).
MSS. Afr. s. 1281(3)

243. JERVIS (T. S.). A history of robusta coffee in Bukoba, n. d. (Reprod. from typescript). (On loan).   MSS. Afr. s. 1416, ff. 29-48

244. JEWELL (G. R.). Various game observation, 1955, as Honorary Game Ranger, Tanganyika. (Typescript).   MSS. Afr. s. 1262

245. JOHNSTON (John Rooke). Bits and pieces, or, Seven years in the Western Province of Tanganyika territory, 1933-1940 as D. O. (Typescript).   MSS. Afr. s. 1270

246. JOHNSTON (Russell R.). American Red Cross reports on Polish refugee camps in Tanganyika, Northern and Southern Rhodesia, 1944. 3 vols., with photographs. (Typescript).   MSS. Afr. r. 116(1-3)

247. *KAHAMA (Clement George). Memorandum as Minister for Commerce and Industry on the Dar es Salaam oil refinery proposals. (Cabinet paper of 1962); E. N. I. and Stanvac refinery proposals, 1962. (Typescript).

248. KERNAHAN (C. S.). Usambara scheme, Tanganyika, progress report, June 1953, annual report, 1953, as Executive Officer; extracts from Usambara und seine Nachbargebiete, by O. Baumann, 1890, and Nachrichten aus der ostafrikanischen Mission, 1895. (Xerox).   MSS. Afr. s. 1196

249. KIRK (C. C.). Correspondence with A. Creech Jones and others as Senior Assistant Accountant, Tanganyika railways, on sisal and alternative agricultural industries to avoid post war depression in East Africa, 1944-46. News cutting, the ground nut scheme, 1947. (Typescript).   MSS. Afr. s. 1184

250. LANNING (Eric C.). Miscellaneous notes, articles and correspondence on archaeology and anthropology, Uganda and Tanganyika, 1949-64 (incl.) Cave and rock shelters of western Uganda; Kibengo earthworks; Rock engravings; Bark cloth hammers; The Sesse Islands; The Oldoway human skeleton, &c. 9 files. (Mainly typescript). (On loan).   MSS. Afr. s. 1329(1-9)

251. LATHAM (Michael Charles). Annual medical report, Kilosa district, 1956, 57; Annual report as Medical Officer (Nutrition), Tanganyika, 1962, with associated papers, one by D. V. Latham. (Reprod. from typescript & xerox). MSS. Afr. s. 1370

252. LAWRENCE (F. Seymour). Tanganyika police service: diaries, 1951, 52; case files, 1938-45; alarms, lectures and miscellaneous police papers. 9 pts.
MSS. Afr. s. 1369

253. *LESLIE (J. A. K.). Tape and transcript of talk regarding service in the Buha district of Tanganyika from 1947.

254. LEWIS (E. A.). Anthropological notes, Masai and kindred tribes, Kenya & Tanganyika (1930-46). (Typescript). MSS. Afr. s. 1241

255. LEWIS (Eric A. W.). File of circular letters, minutes and correspondence, April 1959-Sept. 1961, as President of Tanganyika Civil Servants' Association. (Typescript and some printed). MSS. Afr. s. 1351

256. MACDONA (B. F.). Local leave, diary of a holiday in East Africa, 1936; The diary of an enemy, 1941, account of an official visit to Mogadiscio, Italian Somaliland, as banker; Ethiopian interlude, 1942; Kilimanjaro, 1944; East Africa in wartime, 1944; The bank in relation to post-war colonial development, 1943. 6 pts. (Xerox and typescript). MSS. Afr. s. 1312

257. *MacMICHAEL (Sir Harold). Files of correspondence and papers relating to his service in the Sudan, Tanganyika, Palestine, Malaya, Malta, &c., 1905-46.

258. *MARCHANT (P. J. C.). Two letter books, service in Tanganyika, 1953-54; Letters home, 1950-51. (On long loan).

259. *MASON (H.). Meru land and politics, Tanganyika: two documents, 1953, 55.

260. MATHEWSON (W. G.). Notes on the economy of Ufipa district, Tanganyika, 1965; Central Province, agriculture, annual report, 1956; Kilimanjaro region, 5-year development proposals, 1963, &c. MSS. Afr. s. 1320

261. MAWHOOD (P. N.). Ukerewe district, Tanganyika: xerox copies of Annual report for 1956 and 1957, with Handing over notes, 1958. 3 pts. MSS. Afr. s. 1357

262. MBOZI SUB-DISTRICT. Part of monthly report, Dec. 1918, Mbozi sub-district, New Langenburg district. (Typescript). MSS. Afr. s. 1266

263. MORISON (C. G. T.). The soils of Sukumaland, Tanganyika, 1951, by C. G. T. Morison and B. I. Wright. (Typescript). MSS. Afr. s. 1260

264. MZUMBE, local government training centre. Syllabuses of courses and miscellaneous papers on local government in Tanzania, 1964-67. MSS. Afr. s. 1328

265. NASH (Thomas Arthur M.). Personal diary, Oct. 1927-May 1929, as entomologist, tsetse research, Tanganyika; The Rukuba pagan hunt, 1944, N. Nigeria; Letter home, 1944. MSS. Afr. s. 1162

266. NIHILL (Sir John Harry B.). Tanganyika sisal growers association, minutes of meetings of Central joint council, 1958-61; notes and reports on wages, trade unions, &c.; correspondence, newscuttings. 4 files.   MSS. Afr. s. 1174

267. NORTHERN PROVINCE CONVENTION OF ASSOCIATIONS. Minutes of meetings of the Northern Province Convention of Associations, Arusha, Tanganyika, July 1958-June 1960. (Typescript).   MSS. Afr. s. 1224

268. PAGE (C. Eric). Letters home as subaltern, India, Aug. 1916-Nov. 1917 and June 1918-May 1920; East African Expeditionary Force, Tanganyika, Dec. 1917-June 1918; as officer, Police Department, Tanganyika, Dec. 1920-Mar. 1937. 3 vols.
MSS. Afr. s. 1173

269. *POLLOCK (Hugh Wykeham D.). Letters between H. W. D. Pollock and his wife: Tanganyika administration, 1932-33. (On loan).

270. POTTS (William H.). Tsetse research in Tanganyika territory, 1925-52, as entomologist; Report, three maps of Sukumaland, &c.; The history of Basiya and their origin (Swahili with English transl.). Maps, photographs. (Typescript).
MSS. Afr. s. 1259

271. RAYMOND (W. D.). Reminiscences as Government Chemist, Tanganyika, 1934-50. (Typescript).   MSS. Afr. s. 1375

272. RICHES (E. H.). Correspondence and notes as Executive Officer, Northern Province Labour Utilization Board, Tanganyika, 1958 (with) reports of Committee on proposed Employers' Organisation, July-Sept., 1958. (Typescript).
MSS. Afr. s. 1223

273. *ROWE (Eric George). Tapes and transcript of interview on service in Tanganyika as Minister for Local Government and Administration, 1928-59.

274. *———— Decentralisation to provinces in Tanganyika, 1958. (Typescript).

275. SCRIVENOR (Sir Thomas Vaisey). Official diaries, Jan. 1934-April 1937, as Asst. D. C., Tanganyika; Oct. 20-28, 1937, April 1938-Aug. 1939, as Asst. D. C., Palestine; correspondence and police reports, Palestine, 1937-38; Record of an interview with General Montgomery in Haifa, Jan. 12, 1939. (Typescript).
MSS. Brit. Emp. s. 376-379

276. ———— Tape and transcript of an interview, 1969: Colonial Administrator, Tanganyika, Palestine, Malta, Nigeria, High Commission Territories, Colonial Office, 1934-60.   MSS. Brit. Emp. s. 369

277. STURDY (Donald S.). Tape and transcript of interview concerning agricultural service in Tanganyika, 1926-45. (Typescript, 1969).   MSS. Afr. s. 1331

278. SWYNNERTON (G. H.). Memorandum, game of the Serengeti National Park, 1957, as Game Warden, Tanganyika; A report on the grazing potential of the grassland of the Serengeti National Park, 1957, by T. O. Robson, Pasture Research Officer. (Typescript).   MSS. Afr. s. 1238

279. *TANGANYIKA EUROPEAN CIVIL SERVANTS' ASSOCIATION. Minute books, 1947–62. 4 vols.

280. TANGANYIKA POLICE COLLEGE. Lecture notes, Tanganyika Police College (&) Police Training School, Moshi, 1958–61. (Typescript). MSS. Afr. s. 1205

281. TAWNEY (John Jeffery). Diaries, 1940–46, autobiographical writings, reports, broadcast scripts, &c., of service in Tanganyika, 1930–1952. 9 vols. (On loan). MSS. Afr. s. 1333

282. *——— Family letters home from Tanganyika in the 1960's.

283. TRANT (H.). With a medical survey, Ukara Island, Tanganyika, 1950–51. (Typescript). MSS. Afr. s. 1362(1–3)

284. TREMBETH (Rosalie). The making of a mountaineer, account of a journey to Kilimanjaro, 1941. (Typescript). MSS. Afr. s. 1154

285. *TRIPE (William Borrowdale). Letters to his parents, reports and memoranda, &c., 1928–45 while a colonial administrator in Tanganyika and including war service in the Middle East. 4 boxes.

286. TURNER (D. B.). Tsetse survey and reclamation, Tanganyika, 1956–62. 5 typewritten papers. MSS. Afr. s. 1376

287. *VINTER (J. S. M.). Tape and transcript of interview: colonial service administration in Tanganyika, 1947–63.

288. *WALL (J.) Report of confidential meeting in Dar es Salaam, Nov. 16, 1960, with P. Rogers, Asst. Under Secretary of State, to discuss post–independence conditions of service, compensation, &c., for East Africa High Commission officers in Tanganyika. (Typescript).

289. WAYLAND (E. J.). The age of the Oldoway (Tanganyika) human skeleton, 1932, as Director of Geological Survey. (Typescript). (On loan). MSS. Afr. s. 1329(10)

290. WILLIAMSON (John Thorburn). The Williamson diamond mine, Tanganyika, publ. 1958, by East Africa and Rhodesia: Notes on the geology of Mwadui diamond field, 1949; Background material for the press and radio visit, 1959; Memorandum by Commissioner for mines on the Oppenheimer proposals for a new purchasing agreement with Williamson Diamonds, Ltd., 1955. (Typescript). MSS. Afr. s. 1281(5)

291. *YOUNG (R. W.). Police diaries and notebooks, Tanganyika, 1952, 54–58. (On loan).

292. *YOUNG (Mrs. R. W.). Personal letters written home when teaching in the Education Department of Tanganyika, 1953–55.

UGANDA

293. ARROWSMITH (Keith V.). Diaries as Administrative Officer, Nigeria, 1949, 50, 53-54; as D. O., Uganda, 1957, 59, 61; Much in little (autobiography), 1968. 6 vols. (On long loan).   MSS. Afr. s. 1338

294. BAKER (Clement John). Diaries, 1901, 1902, 1904, 1908 and 1909, and papers as Medical and Sanitary officer in Uganda, 1902-28. 4 boxes.   MSS. Afr. s. 1091

295. BRUTON (Charles Lamb). Joint select committee on East Africa (closer union), preliminary statement, with associated memoranda, correspondence, &c., 1930-31; The Basoga; The Baganda; The Batwa; West Nile border disturbances, report, 1921; Letters from Africans, 1927-57 (Uganda). 6 files.   MSS. Afr. s. 1366

296. CLEAVE (J.). Survey of Moroto mountain, Uganda: population survey in memorandum to the District Commissioner, Karamoja, 1958. (Photostat).
   MSS. Afr. s. 1354

297. COOTE (John Methuen). Diary, Bukedi district, Uganda, a tour in the Teso country, the Kivu mission and Mbale residency, 1909-11, with correspondence with H. B. Thomas on the Kivu mission, 1955-57. 2 vols.   MSS. Afr. s. 1383

298. CORYDON (Sir Robert Thorne). Correspondence, memoranda, &c., as Governor of Uganda, 1917-22; as Governor of Kenya, 1923-25; biographical material; Church Missionary Society correspondence, Kikuyu and land question, Kenya, 1903-47. 18 boxes.   MSS. Afr. s. 633

299. DEPARTMENT OF AGRICULTURE. Miscellaneous reports (incl.) Symposium on mechanical cultivation in Uganda, 17-19 Dec., 1958; Annual reports of Special development section, 1956, 62, 63; Procedure notes for group farm managers; Analysis of (farm) records, Mar. 1959-Mar. 1960. 3 vols. (Typescript).
   MSS. Afr. s. 1209

300. ELLIOT (James Robert McD.). Diaries, notes and memoirs as D. O. and Provincial Commissioner, Uganda, 1920-45: Toro, Kigesi, Bugishu, Teso, Bugwere districts; The Nabingi, an anti-European secret society in British Ruanda and Ndorwa, by T. Philipps.   MSS. Afr. s. 1384

301. *FLEMING (J. T.). Miscellaneous legal papers, Uganda, 1957-65. 2 files. (On long loan).

302. *GEE (T. W.). Educational papers, Uganda, 1964. 2 vols.

303. GOWERS (Sir William Frederick). Correspondence, 1927-32, as Governor of Uganda; diary of a visit to the Belgian Congo, Apr. 18-May 3, 1931; miscellaneous notes on African affairs, &c. 11 pts. (Mainly typescript).   MSS. Afr. s. 1150

304. GRIFFIN (Sir John Bowes). The Kabaka case, civil case no. 50 of 1954; in H. M. High Court of Uganda, before the Hon. J. B. Griffin, Chief Justice (with) explanatory note. (Typescript).   MSS. Afr. s. 1208

305. HARRIS (David L.). Notes on the early history of the West Nile district of Uganda, with map, 1959. (Xerox).   MSS. Afr. s. 1350

306. *HENDERSON (D. S.). Diary and notes as a police officer during the Buganda rising in 1966. (Xerox).

307. KABAKA. Report of the Commission appointed to examine the financial position of the Kabaka's government, its staffing arrangements and salaries in the light of the present economic situation, with Governor's reply, 1961. (Reprod. from typescript).   MSS. Afr. s. 1419

308. LANE (Peter Nigel). Instructions and circulars to County and Divisional Chiefs, West Nile District, Uganda, concerning Legislative Council elections, 1961, National Assembly elections, 1962, as D. C. Map. (Typescript). MSS. Afr. s. 1240

309. LANNING (Eric C.). Miscellaneous notes, articles and correspondence on arch-aeology and anthropology, Uganda and Tanganyika, 1949-64 (incl.) Cave and rock shelters of western Uganda; Kibengo earthworks; Rock engravings; Bark cloth hammers; The Sesse Islands; The Oldoway human skeleton, &c. 9 files. (Mainly typescript). (On loan).   MSS. Afr. s. 1329

310. McCUMISKEY (J. L.). Miscellaneous notes and reports as farm manager, Uganda: Busoga farms; Bukalasa farm institute; Namalere, 1955-65. Farm man-agement, radio talk to schools. (Typescript).   MSS. Afr. s. 1226

311. MANKIN (J. H.). Minutes of a meeting of the Central Town Planning Board, Entebbe, Uganda, 11 Dec., 1946. (Typewritten).   MSS. Afr. s. 1398

312. MARRIOTT (J.). Notes on service with the Government of Uganda as Education Officer, 1956 to 1965. (Typescript).   MSS. Afr. r. 111

313. MASEFIELD (Charles J. B.). Letter to his Mother containing references to the Uganda martyrs, June 19, 1894.   MSS. Afr. s. 424, ff. 557-559

314. MASEFIELD (Geoffrey Bussell). Agricultural extension methods amongst African peasant farmers, as Agricultural Officer, Uganda (1948). (Typescript).
                   MSS. Afr. s. 1225

315. MAYBURY (Maurice A.). Uganda credit and savings bank, its purpose and functions, 1958.   MSS. Afr. s. 1405(1)

316. ———— The Uganda credit and savings bank, memorandum for the Economic development committee, 1959. (Both reprod. from typescript). MSS. Afr. s. 1405(2)

317. MIDDLETON (John Francis M.). Report on the Lugbara people of Uganda and Belgian Congo, with special reference to labour migration, 1951. (Typescript).
                   MSS. Afr. s. 1220

318. *MORRIS (Barbara). Some journeys (in Africa and the Western Pacific), 1958-66. (Typescript, with 4 volumes of photographs).

319. NEATBY (Helen M. J.). Note book on school visits, 1944-47, as Asst. Director of Education, Uganda; notes and correspondence (incl.) Memorandum on the education of women and girls, submitted by the Sub-committee of the A.C.A.E. appointed to consider the question, 1953. MSS. Afr. s. 1234

320. OBOTE (Apollo Milton). Typed directive, signed, to R. D. Cordery, Administrator, Fort Portal, Uganda, concerning the exercise of his powers in the areas of Toro under the state of emergency, Apr. 27, 1963. MSS. Afr. s. 424, f. 536

321. ORMSBY (Sydney William). Letters home as D. C. , Uganda, 1897-1908; personal letter from the Governor, H. Hesketh-Bell, 28th Dec. , 1906; report of journey from Nimule to Mbale, 1908. Memorial volume, 21st Jan. , 1909 (with) extracts from letters, photographs. MSS. Afr. r. 105

322. PHILIPPS (James E. T.). The Nabingi, an anti-European secret society in Africa in British Ruanda and Ndorwa (1920). (Typescript). MSS. Afr. s. 1384, ff. 474-493

323. RAWSON (P. H.). Miscellaneous memoranda and reports upon medical matters in Uganda and Nigeria, 1922-29. MSS. Afr. s. 1421

324. *SCOTT (Sir Robert). Personal correspondence: Uganda, Kenya, Gold Coast, Palestine, Mauritius, 1928-58.

325. WILLIS (John Jamieson), Bp. of Uganda. Journal of first tour as a missionary in Uganda, Aug. 30, 1900-Oct. 18, 1902. MSS. Afr. s. 1296

ZANZIBAR

326. ASQUITH (Julian Edward G. , 2nd Earl of Oxford and Asquith). Tape and transcript of interview: service in Palestine, Zanzibar, St. Lucia and Seychelles, 1942-67. (Typescript, 1969). MSS. Brit. Emp. s. 375

327. CAMPBELL (George B.). African witchdoctors, 1951-53; Survey plan of Kimberley mine, 1883 (photostat); British consulate, Zanzibar, 1900: photograph of members. MSS. Afr. s. 1393

328. DAVIES (Vera M.). Zanzibar Welfare Office, miscellaneous papers, 1954-59; African budget survey, Dar es Salaam, Tanganyika, 1956/57. MSS. Afr. s. 1317

329. EVANS (Cecily). The Rockefeller yellow fever commission's expedition to Kukuruku, Nigeria, 1928, as wife of G. A. Williams, D. C. ; Notes for future guidance on the visit of H. R. H. the Princess Margaret to Zanzibar, 1956, as Executive Officer, Royal visit. (Typescript). MSS. Afr. s. 1165

330. MAYHEW (T.). Zanzibar elections, 1957; Tanga (urban) division, annual report, 1960. (Typescript). MSS. Afr. s. 1361(1, 2)

SOUTH AFRICA (in general, comprising four or more territories)

331. BOWER (Sir Graham John). Correspondence, 1898-1951 (incl. letters from)
Cecil Rhodes; J. C. Smuts, 1950; Herbert Baker, 1927; Le Roux Smith Le Roux,
1957-59 with Maude Bower (daughter). Reminiscences of the Jameson Raid
(xerox), by Maude L. Bower (wife). (Some typescript). Photographs.
MSS. Afr. s. 1279

332. BRITISH SOUTH AFRICA COMPANY. Notes on the registration of mining titles:
the formation of the British South Africa Company, early grants of prospecting
and mining rights, 1963. (Xerox).　　　　　　　　　MSS. Afr. s. 1181

333. *CHARTER CONSOLIDATED LIMITED. Correspondence, share registers, &c.,
including a few British South Africa Company and more Wernher, Beit Company
papers, 1890-1960.

334. DURNFORD (Edward). Two letters to F. E. Colenso, Jan. 6, 1885, Aug. 5, 1887,
concerning A. W. Durnford (brother) and "A soldier's life and work in South
Africa". Newscuttings.　　　　　　　　　　　MSS. Afr. s. 1293(6)

335. KRAUSE (Frederick Edward T.). A glimpse into the past, a memorandum dealing with some historical events before and after the surrender of Johannesburg,
May 31, 1900. (Typescript).　　　　　　　　　　MSS. Afr. s. 1247

336. POLAK (Henry Salomon L.). Miscellaneous articles and correspondence on the
Indian question in South and East Africa, 1906-44; Correspondence and memoranda on the Fiji sugar growers dispute, 1943. (On loan).　MSS. Brit. Emp. s. 372

337. ────── The Asiatic passive resistance movement in South Africa, 1908. (Typescript).　　　　　　　　　　　　　　　　　MSS. Afr. r. 125

338. RHODES (Cecil John). Xerox copies of five letters to Sir Robert Herbert, Per-
manent Under Secretary of State for the Colonies, concerning progress of the
pioneer column, Kruger's opposition, Portuguese intentions, necessity to occupy
Mashonaland, Dec. 1889; with three letters (incompl.) from unknown correspond-
ents to Herbert, 1892.　　　　　　　　　　MSS. Afr. t. 14, ff. 113-141

339. RIXON ( ). Typescript of an interview conducted by J. Spicer, Editor of the
Times of Swaziland, with Mr. Rixon, one-time valet to C. J. Rhodes, 1950.
MSS. Afr. s. 424, ff. 537-545

340. ROOS (J. C.). Half a century ago. Anglo-Boer war, 1899-1902: the surrender
of Johannesburg, May 31, 1900, how Johannesburg and the mines were saved.
(Reprod. from typescript).　　　　　　　　　　MSS. Afr. s. 1245

341. SMUTS (Jan Christiaan). Typed copies of correspondence with the Clark family,
including M. C. and A. B. Gillett, 1905-50. 29 files.　　MSS. Afr. s. 1414

342. STANLEY (Sir Herbert James). Correspondence, 1910-41, and memoranda
(incl.) report of an informal discussion with General Smuts, 1910;　the

constitutional question in Southern Rhodesia (c. 1920), as Imperial Secretary, South Africa; on the Bledisloe report (c. 1937), as Governor, Southern Rhodesia. (Mainly typescript). MSS. Afr. s. 1250

343. WIENAND (Carlie E.). Reminiscences (Northern Rhodesia, 1874-1906, incl. account of Cecil Rhodes's funeral), typescript of tape recording made at Broken Hill; Reminiscences of the last of the Zeederbergers, coaching days, 1896-97. (Typescript, on loan). MSS. Afr. s. 1314(3, 4)

344. WILBERFORCE (Samuel), successively Bishop of Oxford and of Winchester. Letters concerning the church in Central Africa, 1860-66; in South Africa, 1856 -73. (B) MS. Wilberforce c. 19, f. 1, 40

345. ———— Notes on the 'Colenso affair' (1853). (B) MS. Wilberforce c. 25, f. 102

346. ———— Letters to Robert Gray, Bishop of Cape Town, 1861-71. (B) MS. Wilberforce d. 39

BASUTOLAND/LESOTHO

347. *HECTOR (Gordon Matthews). Memoranda, notes, correspondence, &c., on military service in East Africa; as an administrator in Kenya, the Seychelles and in Basutoland as Leader of the House, 1940-67.

348. SANDERS (P. B.). The Basutoland general election, 1965, draft of report as Chief Electoral Officer. (Reprod. from typescript). MSS. Afr. s. 1308

349. SCHREINER (William Philip). Letter to F. E. Colenso, Aug. 25, 1909, concerning Basutoland and the Bechuanaland Protectorate; letters to Sophie Colenso, Aug. 1-8, 1918, an enquiry about an alleged son of Cetywayo. MSS. Afr. s. 1293(7)

350. SIMS (James Hugh). Notebooks, the story of my life, 1878-(c. 1964); Basutoland reminiscences, 1905-1938, story of career in the Civil Service as written for Basutoland News. 4 vols. (Part typescript). MSS. Afr. s. 1155

BECHUANALAND/BOTSWANA

351. DOUGLAS (Arthur John A.). Miscellaneous reports and memoranda concerning Gaberones as new capital city, Bechuanaland Protectorate, 1961-65, as Chief Secretary; Transfer of Govt. H. Q. from Mafeking; Reorganisation of government in Gaberones; Preparations for elections, Mar. 1, 1965. 13 files. Maps, plans. (Typescript). (On long loan). MSS. Afr. s. 1256

352. ELLENBERGER (Jules). Miscellaneous reports, correspondence and recollections of Bechuanaland, 1892-1950, as Resident Magistrate. MSS. Afr. s. 1198(2)

353. ELLENBERGER (Vivien Frederic). Ngamiland, annual report, 1931, &c., as Resident Magistrate, Bechuanaland; Seretse Khama's succession, report of a tribal meeting, 1949; reports and correspondence, Bakwena-Bangwaketse boundary, 1880-1960. News cuttings. (Mainly typescript). MSS. Afr. s. 1198(1)

354. KHAMA (Tshekedi). Press statement, May 25, 1951, concerning the banishment of Tshekedi and Seretse Khama from Bechuanaland. (Typescript).

MSS. Afr. s. 1249

355. *——— The proposed inclusion of Bechuanaland into the Union of South Africa, June 1, 1954. (Typescript, with notes in his hand).

356. RATSHOSA (Simon). My book on Bechuanaland Protectorate, native custom, etc. (c. 1885-1930). (Unpubl. typescript). MSS. Afr. s. 1198(3)

357. *REDMAN (N. V.). Bamangwato African Authority, Bechuanaland Protectorate: appeal to the Secretary of State, Feb. 1951, concerning the banishment of Seretse Khama; Address by the Resident Commissioner in the Serowe Kgotla (c. 1951) on the succession of the Chieftainship of the Bamangwato tribe; Draft statement on economic development, 1962. (Typescript).

358. SCHREINER (William Philip). Letter to F. E. Colenso, Aug. 25, 1909, concerning Basutoland and the Bechuanaland Protectorate; letters to Sophie Colenso, Aug. 1-8, 1918, an enquiry about an alleged son of Cetywayo. MSS. Afr. s. 1293(7)

359. *SILLERY (Anthony). Bechuanaland reminiscences of a colonial civil servant, 1947-50.

CAPE OF GOOD HOPE

360. CAMPBELL (George B.). African witchdoctors, 1951-53; Survey plan of Kimberley mine, 1883 (photostat); British consulate, Zanzibar, 1900: photograph of members. MSS. Afr. s. 1393

361. MACARTNEY (George, 1st Earl). Letter-book into which have been inserted letters from Britain to the Cape, 1797-98, mainly instructions to Macartney. In microfilm. Micr. Afr. 511

362. PHILIP (John). Conflict with Lord Charles Somerset; The settlement at the Cape to the discovery of the Bethelsdorp letters, being notes on the John Philip papers in the Library of the University of the Witwatersrand, Johannesburg, 1819-21. 2 pts. (Xerox). MSS. Afr. t. 18

363. WILBERFORCE (Samuel), successively Bishop of Oxford and of Winchester. Letters concerning the church in Central Africa, 1860-66; in South Africa, 1856-73. (B) MS. Wilberforce c. 19, f. 1, 40

364. ——— Notes on the 'Colenso affair' (1853). (B) MS. Wilberforce c. 25, f. 102

365. ———— Letters to Robert Gray, Bishop of Cape Town, 1861-71.

(B) MS. Wilberforce d. 39

HIGH COMMISSION TERRITORIES

366. *DOUGLAS (A. J. A.). Ministers' guidance file, High Commission Territories, 1965.

367. *LATIMER (Sir Robert). Tape and transcript of interview: service in the High Commission Territories of southern Africa, 1949-64.

368. SCRIVENOR (Sir Thomas Vaisey). Tape and transcript of an interview, 1969: Colonial Administrator, Tanganyika, Palestine, Malta, Nigeria, High Commission Territories, Colonial Office, 1934-60. MSS. Brit. Emp. s. 369

NATAL & ZULULAND

369. BAINES (Frederick Samuel), Bp. of Natal. The Church properties bill, speeches, July 7, 1903, by Bishop Baines and G. A. de R. Labistour in the Legislative Assembly, Natal. (Typescript). MSS. Afr. s. 1293(3)

370. CHURCH OF ENGLAND IN NATAL. Miscellaneous correspondence, 1901-1909 (incl.) copy of letter from the Archbishop of Canterbury, July 13, 1903: Annual meeting of Maritzburg Mission Association, 1903; Notes and memoranda; Draft petition, 1909, to the Legislative Assembly of the Colony of Natal. News cuttings. MSS. Afr. s. 1292

371. COLENSO (Agnes Mary). Letters from Natal, 1876-1930, mainly to her brother, F. E. Colenso, concerning native affairs. MSS. Afr. s. 1287

372. COLENSO (Emily). Letters from Natal, 1881-1923 (mainly) to F. E. Colenso (brother in law), incl. letter, July 8th, 1883, describing Bishop Colenso's last illness and death. MSS. Afr. s. 1290

373. COLENSO (Frances Ellen). Letters from Natal, mainly to F. E. Colenso (brother), 1876-87, concerning A. W. Durnford, killed at Isandhlwana, Cetywayo, the Zulus, &c.; miscellaneous correspondence, 1885-86; MS. of introduction and preface to "The ruin of Zululand", 1884. News cuttings, review of the book. MSS. Afr. s. 1288

374. COLENSO (Frances Sarah). Letters from Natal, 1878-93, as wife of Bishop Colenso (mainly) to their son, Francis Ernest, on family matters; copy of letters, 1884, from B. Jowett and others to W. E. Gladstone, requesting a pension; Letters of condolence on her death, Jan. 1894. MSS. Afr. s. 1284

375. COLENSO (Francis Ernest). Letters to his wife Sophie, 1876-1910 (from Natal, 1877-79. March-May, 1900); Letter books and general correspondence, 1879-

1909, concerning Bishop Colenso, church affairs, native problems. Photographs.
News cuttings. 17 vols. MSS. Afr. s. 1285

376. COLENSO (Harriette Emily). Letters from Natal, 1876-1930, mainly to F. E.
Colenso (brother) on native affairs and church matters; miscellaneous official
correspondence, 1884-1929, with George Cox, A. G. Shepstone, Arthur Have-
lock, &c. MSS. Afr. s. 1286

377. COLENSO (John William), Bp. of Natal. Letters to F. E. Colenso (son) from
Natal, 1876-81; incomplete copy of correspondence, Jan. 1883, on the communi-
cant test; brief details of career. 3 vols. of news cuttings. Photographs.
MSS. Afr. s. 1283

378. COLENSO (Robert John). Letters from Natal, 1876-1924 (mainly) to F. E.
Colenso (brother), incl. letter, June 25, 1883, concerning the death of Bishop
Colenso. MSS. Afr. s. 1289

379. COLENSO (Sophie Jeanetta). Letters to Francis Ernest Colenso (husband), 1876
-1909, from England and Germany; letters from their children, 1886-1910; other
personal correspondence (incl. letters from) Ramsay Macdonald, E. D. Morel &
P. H. Wicksteed, 1912-13. 9 vols. MSS. Afr. s. 1291

380. COLLEY (Archdeacon Thomas). Proceedings in the Supreme Court of Natal.
April 10, 1888; resignation of his offices as Archdeacon of Pietermaritzburg,
Canon of St. Peters Cathedral, Administrator of the Diocese of Natal and Offic-
iating Minister of St. Peters. MSS. Afr. s. 1293(2)

381. COX (Sir George William). Correspondence, 1883-1905 (mainly) with the Colenso family, concerning the See of Natal and "The life of Bishop Colenso".
Newspaper reviews. MSS. Afr. s. 1293(4)

382. FYNNEY (Oswald Henry B.). Correspondence, Feb. 8-Mar. 1, 1926, as Chief
Magistrate, North Zululand, concerning transfer to Pinetown, South Africa;
Letter to G. Heaton Nicholls, March 15, 1927, on the Zulu marriage and succes-
sion system. MSS. Afr. s. 1310

383. LABISTOUR (G. A. de Roquefeuil). The Church properties bill, speeches, July 7,
1903, by Bishop Baines and G. A. de R. Labistour in the Legislative Assembly,
Natal. (Typescript). MSS. Afr. s. 1293(3)

384. NATAL DIOCESE. Copy of first order in the Supreme Court of Natal, Sept. 27,
1884, to appoint curators of the diocesan properties and fund; second order, Dec.
1, 1884, to authorise the curators to apply a sufficient part of the income to make
necessary payments for the support of the church and schools. MSS. Afr. s. 1293(1)

385. SCHREINER (Olive Emilie). Letter to F. E. Colenso, Sept. 23, 1908, concerning
Dinuzulu and inaccurate reporting of native trials; letters to Sophie Colenso,
1914-19 on personal matters. MSS. Afr. s. 1293(8)

386. SCHREINER (William Philip). Letter to F. E. Colenso, Aug. 25, 1909, concerning Basutoland and the Bechuanaland Protectorate; letters to Sophie Colenso, Aug. 1-8, 1918, an enquiry about an alleged son of Cetywayo.   MSS. Afr. s. 1293(7)

387. WILBERFORCE (Samuel), successively Bishop of Oxford and of Winchester. Letters concerning the church in Central Africa, 1860-66; in South Africa, 1856-73.   (B) MS. Wilberforce c. 19, f. 1, 40

388. ———— Notes on the 'Colenso affair' (1853).   (B) MS. Wilberforce c. 25, f. 102

389. ———— Letters to Robert Gray, Bishop of Cape Town, 1861-71.
(B) MS. Wilberforce d. 39

SWAZILAND

390. BRUTON (Charles Lamb). Memorandum of my impressions of Swaziland during my period as Resident Commissioner, with correspondence & letters &c. from Africans, 1937-68. 2 files.   MSS. Afr. s. 1366(7, 8)

391. *FAIRLIE (M. J.). Swaziland: aims of government policy, Africans in the civil service, future steps in Swaziland, &c., 1960, 62.

392. HIGH COURT. Oath book, Dec. 6, 1904 - March 24, 1954 (with) index.
MSS. Afr. s. 1206

393. PRISON ROLL. Prison roll, 1927-33; Lubuli criminal record book, 1936-44; Civil cases file, 1960-64. 3 vols.   MSS. Afr. s. 1339-1341

394. WILSON (J. B.). Swaziland: Manpower assessment; Annual report, Labour Commissioner; Report on job evaluation; Handing over notes, 1964-65. 4 pts. (Typescript).   MSS. Afr. s. 1349

TRANSVAAL

395. BERNSTEIN (Solomon N.). Early history of the University of Witwatersrand, Transvaal, 1896-1922. (Typescript).   MSS. Afr. s. 1246

WEST AFRICA (in general, comprising four or more territories)

396. JACKSON (J.). Report upon the work of the Land boundary commission, with especial emphasis on matters relating to the settlement and registration of titles to land (Ghana), 1960; Explanatory notes upon the Courts act, 1960; Notes for talks on West African matters. (Typescript). MSS. Afr. s. 1297

397. *PATTERSON (Rt. Rev. Cecil John). Tape and transcript of interview with Dr. Patterson, formerly missionary in Southern Nigeria, Bishop on the Niger and Archbishop of West Africa, 1934-69.

398. *SOUTHGATE (S. J. E.). Tapes and transcript of interview: Colonial Office; West African Inter-territorial Secretariat; Commonwealth Sugar Exporters, 1947-69.

GAMBIA

399. BURKINSHAW (P. L.). Gambia: History of Bathurst, 1955; Handing over notes, Upper River division, 1956, 1958; Notes on native law and customs, n. d. 4 pts. (Typescript). MSS. Afr. s. 1407(2)

400. GAMBIA. Letter book, British Kombo, 1897-1900; Travelling Commissioners' reports, 1893-1922; Reports, S. Bank & N. Bank Province, Kombo & Foni Province, &c., 1900-33. (In microfilm, 7 reels; originals in Gambia Government Archives). List in Box 1. Micr. Afr. 485

401. HODGSON (Peter Charles). Miscellaneous notes on political progress in a primitive community; native courts; principles of indirect rule; Ogbeyan intelligence reports, &c., as D. O., Nigeria, 1934-44; as Commissioner, Gambia, 1944-50; Memorandum on N. J. Brooke's report on the native court system, Sierra Leone (c. 1950). MSS. Afr. s. 1215

402. *LETCHWORTH (Thomas Edwin). Tape and transcript of interview on service in Northern Nigeria and the Gambia, 1928-45.

403. MILVERTON (Arthur Frederick, 1st Baron). Tape recording and transcript of an interview, 1969: recollections as a Colonial administrator, service in Malaya, 1908-30; Governor of North Borneo, 1930-33; the Gambia, 1933-36; Fiji and the Western Pacific, 1936-38; Jamaica, 1938-43; Nigeria, 1943-47.

MSS. Brit. Emp. s. 368

404. WEIR (Neil Archibald C.). Personal diary, Nigeria, 1925-36; Sierra Leone, 1936-43; the Gambia, 1943-50, as Administrative Officer; district reports, Nigeria; Native administration notes, Sierra Leone; Lord Hailey's questionnaire, the Gambia, 1948. 9 vols. (Typescript). MSS. Afr. s. 1151

GOLD COAST/GHANA, ASHANTI & TOGOLAND

405. AMHERST (Hon. Humphrey William). Informal district diaries, Northern Territories, Gold Coast, as D. C., Gonja, 1930-38; Dagomba, June-Nov. 1939; Lawra-Tumu, 1940-44; Mamprusi, Apr.-Nov. 1947; Report on the constitution, organisation and customs of the Nanumba people, 1931; Enrobement of a chief, Bole, 1932. (Typescript).   MSS. Afr. s. 1207

406. ASANTEWA (Yah), Queen Mother of Djesu. Letter to Sir F. Hodgson, Governor of the Gold Coast, through the Resident of Kumasi, requesting protection against some of the Ashanti Kings, April 19th, 1900.   MSS. Afr. s. 1204(2)

407. BAAKO (Kofi). Ghana's conception of socialism, speech at a seminar for Ghanaian and American students, 1961, as Minister of Parliamentary Affairs. (Typescript).   MSS. Afr. s. 1168

408. BARDSLEY (John). Diaries in typescript, 1949-52, as General Secretary of the Christian Council of the Gold Coast and member of the Legislative Council. 4 vols.   MSS. Afr. r. 119-122

409. BEATTIE (Andrew Gordon). Papers &c., chiefly concerning material, 1953-58, for a book on Agriculture and land use in Ghana, published in 1962. 2 boxes.
                                                                 MSS. Afr. s. 1122

410. *BEETON (William Hugh). Tapes and transcripts of an interview between A. J. Loveridge and W. H. Beeton with A. H. M. Kirk-Greene, 1968, on the administration of the Gold Coast, as D. C. s and Chief Commissioners, Ashanti, 1930-56 and 1926-54 respectively.

411. BENNION (F. A. R.). A note on the application in civil proceedings in Ghana of English law and customary law, 1960. (Reprod. from typescript).
                                                                 MSS. Afr. s. 1303

412. BOYLE (David). Letter to Dame Margery Perham, July 10th, 1968, concerning the Queen Mother of Djesu and the Ashanti rising of 1900. (Typescript).
                                                                 MSS. Afr. s. 1204(1)

413. BROWN (Philip Penton). Notes on the canoes of the Gold Coast, 1928 (with) diagrams, as Asst. Master, Achimota. (Typescript).   MSS. Afr. s. 1309

414. CREASY (Sir Gerald Hallen). Tape and transcript of interview: Colonial Office, Governor of the Gold Coast, Governor of Malta, 1920-54. (Typescript).
                                                                 MSS. Brit. Emp. s. 380

415. DOWSON (Sir Ernest Macleod). Registration of title to land with special reference to its introduction on the Gold Coast, 1946, by Sir E. M. Dowson and V. L. O. Sheppard. Pt. 3. (Photostat).   MSS. Afr. s. 1306

416. JACKSON (J.). Report upon the work of the Land boundary commission, with especial emphasis on matters relating to the settlement and registration of titles to land (Ghana), 1960; Explanatory notes upon the Courts act, 1960; Notes for talks on West African matters. (Typescript). MSS. Afr. s. 1297

417. JAQUES (E. H.). Typed copies of personal diaries and letters: Gold Coast, work with mining companies, 1933-39, 2 vols.; Military service, 1939-42, 2 vols.; Northern Nigeria, as geologist, 1942-47, 2 vols.; Cameroons, 1948-50, 2 vols.
MSS. Afr. s. 1385

418. KIRK (J. B.). Diary of tours in the Gold Coast, as Director of Medical Services, 1942, 43. MSS. Afr. s. 1368

419. ——— Some general considerations arising out of the tours, 1942; Memoranda on training of hospital nurses, policy of preventive medicine, recruitment for medical service, 1943. 4 pts. (Typewritten). MSS. Afr. s. 1402

420. KOKOMLEMLE CONSOLIDATED CASES. West African Court of appeal, March 4, 1955: appeal, in 16 consolidated actions, against the judgment of J. Jackson in the Land Court, Accra. (Reprod. from typescript). MSS. Afr. s. 1304

421. LAND TENURE. Customary land tenure in the Gold Coast, replies to queries by the Government, Sept. 1912, by the Paramount Chiefs of Eastern Akim and Akwapem. (Typescript). MSS. Afr. s. 1298

422. LEWEY (Arthur). Opinion, as Attorney-General, for the Colonial Secretary, Nov. 20, 1944, concerning the ownership of minerals on the sea bed in Gold Coast territorial waters. (Photostat). MSS. Afr. s. 1305

423. LLOYD (L. Gordon). Diary, 1925-27, as Asst. Engineer, Gold Coast Government Railways, 2 vols.; Hunting trip in Ashanti and Northern Territories, April, 1928; miscellaneous letters requesting promotion, money, &c., 1925-35; European correspondence, 1927-37 (incl.) 2 letters from R. S. Rattray. Photographs. 4 vols.
MSS. Afr. s. 1242

424. LOVERIDGE (Arthur John). Memorandum on areas of jurisdiction, 1946, as Judicial Adviser, Gold Coast; Tribal jurisdiction and land ownership in the Gold Coast, 1948. (Typescript). MSS. Afr. s. 1302

425. *——— Tapes and transcripts of an interview between A. J. Loveridge and W. H. Beeton with A. H. M. Kirk-Greene, 1968, on the administration of the Gold Coast, as D. C. s and Chief Commissioners, Ashanti, 1930-56 and 1926-54 respectively.

426. POPE (Stead). Reminiscences, 1913-67 (mainly) as District Surveyor, Posts and Telegraphs, Gold Coast, 1913-14; Togoland Field Force, Aug. 1914-April 1915. (Xerox). MSS. Afr. s. 1275

427. RODGER (Sir John). Miscellaneous extracts from notes on territorial rights, land ownership, &c., Gold Coast, 1908-18, by Sir John Rodger, Sir Hugh Clifford (Governors) and F. Crowther, Secretary of Native Affairs. (Typescript).
MSS. Afr. s. 1300

428. RUSSELL (Arthur Colin). Papers concerned with the years that immediately preceded the grant of independence to the Gold Coast in 1957: the National Liberation Movement, native courts, elections, constitutional reform, &c., 1946-57. 5 boxes.   MSS. Afr. s. 1111

429. *SCOTT (Sir Robert). Personal correspondence: Uganda, Kenya, Gold Coast, Palestine, Mauritius, 1928-58.

430. STACPOOLE (G. W.). Registration of title, 1944, as Commissioner of Lands, Gold Coast. (Typescript).   MSS. Afr. s. 1299

431. TYRIE (J. P.). Miscellaneous circulars from the Colonial Secretary, Gold Coast, 1950-54: Operational orders, 1956-59 as Superintendent of Police (incl.) Special police duties and itinerary for the visit to Ghana of the Duke of Edinburgh, 1959. (Typescript).   MSS. Afr. s. 1280

432. VOYAGES AND TRAVELS. Voyages and travels (published by His Majesty's authority, 1743), by unidentified merchant. (Typescript).   MSS. Afr. s. 1301

433. WARD (William Ernest F.). My Africa, reminiscences as a master, Achimota College, Gold Coast, 1924-40. (Xerox).   MSS. Afr. r. 127

434. WILKINSON (Mrs. D. G.). Personal cash book, as teacher, Achimota school, Gold Coast, June 1941-Aug. 1942.   MSS. Afr. s. 1258

435. *WILMOT (A. T. de B.). Reports, correspondence, despatches, Secretariat and Ministerial minutes: Northern Rhodesia, Gold Coast, Colonial Development Corporation, c. 1930-60. (On loan).

NIGERIA & CAMEROONS

436. ABADIE (George). Nigerian letters, 1897-1904. (Typescript. On loan).   MSS. Afr. s. 1337

437. *ALLEN (James Godfrey C.). Nigerian panorama, 1926-66, a District Officer from Eastern Nigeria looks back. (Typewritten).

438. ARNETT (Edward John). Correspondence, reports, memoranda as an administrative officer: Crown Agents; Revenue officer, Nigeria; Resident in Northern Nigeria; Senior Resident of Sokoto, &c., 1902-40. 10 boxes.   MSS. Afr. s. 952

439. ARROWSMITH (Keith V.). Diaries as Administrative Officer, Nigeria, 1949, 50, 53-54; as D. O., Uganda, 1957, 59, 61; Much in little (autobiography), 1968. 6 vols. (On long loan).   MSS. Afr. s. 1338

440. BAIN (Alexander David N.). Reports and memoranda on water supply, Nigeria, 1931-38, as geologist; extracts from informal diary, Aug. 1923-July 1929, Dec. 1939-Jan. 1940; letters home, 1926-38; letters home from Rena Bain (wife), 1931 -37. Maps.   MSS. Afr. s. 1152

441. *BALEWA (Sir Abubakar Tafawa). Document concerning a coalition government in 1959, with translation and letter of explanation by Sir Peter Stallard.

442. ———— Speech by the Prime Minister of the Federation of Nigeria at the independence ceremony on 1st Oct., 1960. (Typescript).   MSS. Afr. s. 1219

443. BARBER (W.). A memorandum on the water supply of part of Askira district, Biu Division, Nigeria, 1958, as geologist. (Typescript).   MSS. Afr. s. 1268

444. BELCHER (Margaret L.). Letters home as Social Welfare Officer, Calabar, Nigeria, 1948-58; letter to Resident, Calabar, on slave dealing and child stealing, 1952; notes on child care and protection cases, 1951-58.   MSS. Afr. s. 1343

445. *BELL (Sir Gawain). Tape and transcript of interview: service in the Sudan and Northern Nigeria, &c., 1931-62.

446. BRIDGES (William Maclaren). Banso re-assessment report (Cameroons), c. 1933. (Typescript).   MSS. Afr. s. 1392

447. ———— Summary of views on (Nigerian) administration, 1947. (Typewritten).
                MSS. Afr. s. 1391

448. BULL (J. C.). Part of the diary of J. C. Bull, an African who worked for the Methodist Minister in charge of the Oron Circuit, Calabar Province, Nigeria, 1919, 22-31. (Typescript).   MSS. Afr. s. 1221

449. CLIFFORD (Sir Hugh Charles). Correspondence, as Governor of Nigeria, to Sir William Gowers, Lieut. Governor, N. Provinces, Nigeria, 1920-24. (Mainly typescript).   MSS. Afr. s. 1149

450. *CLIFFORD (Sir Miles). Tapes and transcript of interview: Nigeria, Gibraltar, Falkland Islands, 1921-54.

451. COLLIER (F. S.). Keepers of the King's forest (uncompleted autobiography); Handing over notes, Ogoja Province and Western Circle, Nigeria, 1928, 35; Annual report, Western Circle, 1935; miscellaneous papers concerning forestry in Nigeria, 1944-56. 9 pts. (On long loan).   MSS. Afr. s. 1330

452. COLLINS (N. C.). Educational policy in Northern Nigeria. Thesis, Dip. Ed., Oxford, 1957. (On long loan).   MSS. Afr. r. 110

453. COUZENS (A. H.). Statement as Commissioner of Labour, Nigeria, to the commission of inquiry into railway labour unrest, 1949; Industrial relations in Nigeria, memorandum, 1950; Dept. of Labour monthly circular, June 1949, Apr. 1950-54; minutes of departmental conference, 1949-54. (Typescript).   MSS. Afr. s. 1377

454. *DALDRY (Sir Leonard Charles). Tape and transcript of interview concerning service with the Nigeria Board of Barclays Bank, D. C. O.; as a member of the Nigerian Railway Corporation; as a Special Member of the House of Representatives and as a Senator, 1929-61.

455. DICKINSON (Hon. Richard Sebastian W.). Typed extracts from letters home as A.D.O., Nigeria, 1922-24. MSS. Afr. r. 118

456. EDWARDES (H.S.W.). Xerox copies of informal diaries, 1905-15, 1921-24, as Asst. Resident, Northern Nigeria. MSS. Afr. r. 106

457. ELGEE (C.H.). The evolution of Ibadan, 1811-1913. (Typescript).
MSS. Afr. s. 1169

458. ELLIOTT (H.P.). Diary as Assistant District Officer, Idoma Division, Northern Nigeria, 1935-36. MSS. Afr. s. 1336

459. ELLIS (Richard White B.). Age of puberty in the tropics, report of investigation carried out in Nigeria, 1949. (Typescript). MSS. Afr. s. 1323

460. ELLISON (Randall Erskine). Tapes and transcript of interview: education service in Northern Nigeria, Somaliland and Tanganyika, 1928-57. (Typescript). (See also HIBBERT (Francis Dennis)). MSS. Afr. s. 1332

461. ENGLEDOW (Sir Frank Leonard). Journals of agricultural tours, Mesopotamia, Nigeria, Trinidad, Malaya, West Indies, East Africa, 1918-57. 14 vols.
MSS. Brit. Emp. s. 373

462. EVANS (Cecily). The Rockefeller yellow fever commission's expedition to Kukuruku, Nigeria, 1928, as wife of G.A. Williams, D.C.; Notes for future guidance on the visit of H.R.H. the Princess Margaret to Zanzibar, 1956, as Executive Officer, Royal visit. (Typescript). MSS. Afr. s. 1165

463. FOSTER (Donald S.). A journey to Lake Chad. (Typescript article, 1951).
MSS. Afr. s. 1186

464. GAILER (J.W.). A national plan for the development of technical education in the Federal Republic of Nigeria, as Federal Adviser on technical education, 1964. (Reprod. from typescript). MSS. Afr. s. 1316

465. GAMBLES (Robert M.). Circular letters from Nigeria, 1949-62, sent by R. and M. Gambles (incl.) account of a holiday trip to the Cameroons, 1958, as Senior Veterinary Research Officer. (Typescript). MSS. Afr. s. 1311

466. GARDNER (G.R.). Report on the Mam cult, Nigeria, 1954 (with) record of conversations with two Mam leaders, appendix A. (Typescript). MSS. Afr. s. 1187

467. GILL (Humphrey Clarendon). Photograph of treaty made by Lord Lugard on behalf of the Royal Niger Company, with the King of Nikki on Nov. 10th, 1894; with account, by H.C. Gill, as Assistant D.O., Nigeria, of how the original came into his hands. MSS. Afr. s. 1182

468. GILLIES (I.A.G.). Handing over notes, Arochuku, Itu districts, Nigeria, 1951-53; The reorganization of the northern part of Calabar division. 4 pts. (Typescript). MSS. Afr. s. 1404

469. GRIER (P. A.). A weekend in Paris, 1951, with two Nigerian Emirs. (Type-written). MSS. Afr. s. 1403

470. HALLAM (W. Keith R.). Typed letter to T. E. Letchworth regarding secondment of Nigerian personnel to police, Leopoldville, Congo, 1961. MSS. Afr. s. 1374

471. HAMMOND (S. A.). Education department, Northern Provinces, Nigeria: notes on pagan schools, training of teachers, &c., 1927. (Xerox). MSS. Afr. s. 1325

472. HANBURY (Harold Greville). Part of (unpubl.) autobiography: Nigeria, 1955-67, as arbitrator on minimum wages, 1955; adviser to Ife University on the new Law Faculty, 1962; Dean of the Law Faculty, Nsukka, 1964-66; Trinidad, Gibraltar.
MSS. Brit. Emp. r. 8

473. *HART (C. A.). Papers, reports, minutes, &c., as Principal of the Nigerian College of Arts, Science and Technology, 1957-63.

474. HEATH (Douglas Frank). African secret societies (Nigeria); Circulars, articles, memoranda, &c., as D. O., Nigeria and in Medical Department, Tanganyika, 1920-62; Election as European Member of the Legislative Council, Tanganyika, 1959; Photographs. 5 vols. MSS. Afr. s. 1342

475. HIBBERT (Francis Dennis). Tapes and transcript of interview: service in Northern Nigeria as Deputy Director of Education and Chairman of the N. Nigerian Public Service Commission, 1929-59. (Typescript). (See also ELLISON (Randall Erskine)). MSS. Afr. s. 1332

476. HODGSON (Peter Charles). Miscellaneous notes on political progress in a primitive community; native courts; principles of indirect rule; Ogbeyan intelligence reports, &c., as D. O., Nigeria, 1934-44; as Commissioner, Gambia, 1944-50; Memorandum on N. J. Brooke's report on the native court system, Sierra Leone (c. 1950). MSS. Afr. s. 1215

477. HOGAN (W. L.). The development of education in Northern Nigeria, 1920-52. (Typescript). MSS. Afr. s. 1358

478. HOSKYNS-ABRAHALL (Lois Jennet). Personal diary, Nigeria, 1947-48.
MSS. Afr. s. 1335

479. HOSKYNS-ABRAHALL (Sir Theo Chandos). Nigeria: personal diaries, 1921-22, Borgu, N. Provinces, as Administrative Officer; 1946-52, W. Provinces/Region, as Chief Commissioner and Lieutenant Governor; Mission to Free French, 1940. 10 vols. MSS. Afr. s. 1334

480. *HUDSON (Rowland Skeffington). Tapes and transcript of record of service in Northern Rhodesia, the Colonial Office African Studies Branch, Northern Nigeria, Ministry of Overseas Development, 1919-66.

481. HUTCHIN (I. E.). Handing over notes, 1956-68, as water engineer, Northern Nigeria; Maru T. T. C. water supply, progress report, Oct. 21-Nov. 30, 1964. Maps, diagrams. (Typescript). MSS. Afr. s. 1255

482. *JAMES (E. S.). The Nigeria-Biafra war; Minorities in Biafra, two memoranda, typewritten, 1969, by N. C. Perkins and E. S. James.

483. JAQUES (E. H.). Typed copies of personal diaries and letters: Gold Coast, work with mining companies, 1933-39, 2 vols.; Military service, 1939-42, 2 vols.; Northern Nigeria, as geologist, 1942-47, 2 vols.; Cameroons, 1948-50, 2 vols.
MSS. Afr. s. 1385

484. JOURDAIN (A. T.). Official and private correspondence, 1954-58 (incl.) notes and letters as representative of John Holt Nigeria Limited and as Special Member of the House of Assembly, Northern Nigeria, unofficial reports of sessions of the House of Assembly, 1956-58. 2 files. (Typescript).   MSS. Afr. s. 1346

485. *KIRK-GREENE (Anthony Hamilton M.). Reports on the Northern Nigeria Regiment, 1905, with associated papers; Commission of inquiry into the Zuru native authority, &c., 1960; The history of Kaduna and the capitals of Northern Nigeria; The rivers of Bornu, &c., n.d. (On loan).

486. ———— Letters home from Nigeria, 1950-65, as Administrative Officer, 1950-57, as Head of Public Administration Dept., Zaria University, 1959-65. (On loan).
MSS. Afr. s. 1313

487. LEEMING (Alfred). A brief history of the foundation of Victoria (Nigeria) and the annexation. (Typescript, 1947).   MSS. Afr. s. 1191

488. *LETCHWORTH (Thomas Edwin). Tape and transcript of interview on service in Northern Nigeria and the Gambia, 1928-45.

489. *LETHEM (Sir Gordon James). Correspondence, reports, papers, &c., relating to service in Nigeria, the Leeward Islands and British Guiana, 1914-46. 22 boxes.

490. *MACPHERSON (Sir John). Tape and transcript of service in Nigeria, Palestine, &c., 1937-59.

491. *MADDOCKS (Sir Kenneth). Copies of letters to Nigeria relating to the Constitutional Conference in progress in London, July-August 1953; Record of a meeting of heads of regional departments, Northern Nigeria, 1957. (Typescript). (On long loan).

492. *MARSHALL (Hedley Herbert). Tape and transcript of interview: Attorney-General, Northern Nigeria, 1954-62; Member of the House of Assembly, House of Chiefs and Executive Council, 1951-62.

493. MATHEWS (Hubert Frank). Letters to his parents as Political Officer and Anthropological Officer, Nigeria, 1910-29; official correspondence, reports, &c., 1912-61. 3 boxes.   MSS. Afr. s. 783

494. MICHIE (Charles Watt). Political situation in the Northern Provinces of Nigeria, 1951, as senior D. O.; Local government reform, Igbomina area, Ekiti area, and Bala and Afon districts, Ilorin Province, 1954; History of Ilorin, by M. Sulu, Ilorin native courts registrar. (5 pts., mainly typescript).   MSS. Afr. s. 1210

495. MILBURN (Stanley). Some notes on the history of Esie (Nigeria) and its stone images, 1933; Stone images, Esie, by F. Daniel, 1933; notes on the development of local crafts and industries, 1935-36; notes on the Oyo Province (c. 1930). (Typescript).   MSS. Afr. s. 1167

496. MILVERTON (Arthur Frederick, 1st Baron). Tape recording and transcript of an interview, 1969: recollections as a Colonial administrator, service in Malaya, 1908-30; Governor of North Borneo, 1930-33; the Gambia, 1933-36; Fiji and the Western Pacific, 1936-38; Jamaica, 1938-43; Nigeria, 1943-47.

MSS. Brit. Emp. s. 368

497. MISAU, Emir of. Letter of appointment of the Emir of Misau, Nigeria, in Arabic, signed by Lord Lugard as Governor-General, 1914.   MSS. Afr. t. 19

498. MORLEY (John A. E.). Colonial service: letters to his Mother from Northern Nigeria, 1937-41; from Eritrea, 1941-44; from Singapore, 1945-47. With Chapters on Nigeria (in typescript). 2 vols.   MSS. Brit. Emp. s. 27

499. NASH (Thomas Arthur M.). Personal diary, Oct. 1927-May 1929, as entomologist, tsetse research, Tanganyika; The Rukuba pagan hunt, 1944, N. Nigeria; Letter home, 1944.   MSS. Afr. s. 1162

500. NORTHERN NIGERIA. Official reports and correspondence relating to the work of Administrative Officers in the Gombe Division, Bauchi Province, Northern Nigeria, 1903-42. (Belonged to T. J. Stevens).   MSS. Afr. s. 834

501. *O'REGAN (J. W. H.). Ceylon, Jamaica, Nigeria: miscellaneous correspondence and papers regarding conditions of service, &c., 1935-60.

502. OVERTON (R. C.). Enyong division: touring diary, May, 1954-March, 1955, as D. O., Nigeria; handing over notes, March, 1955; Mamfe division, Southern Cameroons: handing over notes, March, 1961; native administration estimates, 1960-62; development of local government, 1959; notes on boundary disputes &c. (Typescript). (On long loan).   MSS. Afr. s. 1278

503. *PATTERSON (Rt. Rev. Cecil John). Tape and transcript of interview with Dr. Patterson, formerly missionary in Southern Nigeria, Bishop on the Niger and Archbishop of West Africa, 1934-69.

504. *PERKINS (N. C.). The Nigeria-Biafra war; Minorities in Biafra, two memoranda, typewritten, 1969, by N. C. Perkins and E. S. James.

505. PLUMMER (Gladys). Miscellaneous reports and memoranda on female education in Nigeria and British Cameroons, 1943-51, as Deputy Director of Education (women) incl. the survey, 1945-47, on the social and economic position of women in the British Cameroons. (Typescript).   MSS. Afr. s. 1322

506. POCOCK (Reginald C.). Miscellaneous correspondence on pensions, &c., May 7, 1960-July 17, 1961, as Chairman of the Association of Senior Civil Servants, Nigeria (with) Record of a meeting between H. E. the Governor-General and representatives of the A. S. C. S., 1960. (Typescript).   MSS. Afr. s. 1218

507. POWELL (V. B. V.). Reports on the tour of the Nigerian athletic team in the U.K., 1 June-3 Sept., 1948; Nigerian Olympic Team, Helsinki, 1952, report as Team Manager. (Typescript). MSS. Afr. s. 1229

508. RAWSON (P. H.). Miscellaneous memoranda and reports upon medical matters in Uganda and Nigeria, 1922-29. MSS. Afr. s. 1421

509. ROBERTS (Reginald Arthur). Documents relating to appointment to civil service in Nigeria; letters home as Senior Resident, Onitsha Province, &c., 1895-1928. Albums of photographs and news cuttings. 3 vols. MSS. Afr. s. 1348

510. *ROBERTSON (Algar Ronald W.). Nigeria's suggested H.M. Overseas Civil Service prepared in 1953: with associated papers. (Typescript).

511. *ROGERS (Sir Philip). Tape and transcript of interview: service in Nigeria, Kenya, &c., 1947-63.

512. ROSEVEAR (Donovan Reginald). The Eastern Provinces revisited, 1951, as Inspector General of forests. (Nigerian forests information bulletin, 21/1955).
MSS. Brit. Emp. s. 366(6)

513. SCRIVENOR (Sir Thomas Vaisey). Tape and transcript of an interview, 1969: Colonial Administrator, Tanganyika, Palestine, Malta, Nigeria, High Commission Territories, Colonial Office, 1934-60. MSS. Brit. Emp. s. 369

514. SHARWOOD SMITH (Winifred Joan, Lady). "Uwargida", unpubl. autobiography as wife of D. O. and Governor, Northern Nigeria, 1939-57. (Typescript).
MSS. Afr. r. 108

515. SMITH (J. H.). Touring reports and notes, 1951-54, as A. D. O., Northern Nigeria; touring diary, Dec. 26, 1953-Apr. 1, 1954; Report of an investigation into population movement in Kano Province, 1951; A resettlement scheme in Kiru District, 1952, &c. (Typescript). MSS. Afr. s. 1232

516. SMITH (Peter R.). Letters home from Nigeria, 1913-20; Tanganyika, 1927, as an official in the Posts and Telegraphs Department. MSS. Afr. s. 1233

517. STEVENSON (Neil Stuart). A forest regeneration scheme for British Honduras, 1944; revised by A. F. A. Lamb, 1947; draft criticism of the annual report, 1962; Notes on a visit to Eastern Region, Nigeria, 1958, as forestry adviser.
MSS. Brit. Emp. s. 366

518. STUMPENHUSEN PAYNE (E. G.). Calabar Province, Nigeria. Report, existing wages and the cost of living, 1949; Development in Calabar Province, incl. details of a project for native built cottage hospitals, 1952. MSS. Afr. s. 1197

519. SULU (M.). History of Ilorin, by the Ilorin native courts registrar, 1953. (Typescript). MSS. Afr. s. 1210

520. VANTER (Warner). Nearly two million Northern Nigerians have 'joined up' for war against ignorance, press release regarding the adult literacy campaign, 1958; Statistics of adult literacy class, enrolment and certificates, 1947–63; note on rumours and allegations spread since the Federal elections. (Typescript). MSS. Afr. s. 1172

521. WATT (L. S.). Diary as Administrative Officer, Northern Nigeria, 1960. (On loan). MSS. Afr. s. 1412

522. WATT (Margaret J.). Typed extracts from letters from Nigeria to her father, 1951–60. (On loan). MSS. Afr. s. 1413

523. WEIR (Neil Archibald C.). Personal diary, Nigeria, 1925–36; Sierra Leone, 1936–43; the Gambia, 1943–50, as Administrative Officer; district reports, Nigeria; Native administration notes, Sierra Leone; Lord Hailey's questionnaire, the Gambia, 1948. 9 vols. (Typescript). MSS. Afr. s. 1151

524. WILLIAMS (C. V.). Reports to the Council for technical education and training for overseas countries, East Africa, May 1963; Nigeria, Sept. 1963; Sierra Leone, Nov. 1963; Draft minutes of the 8th meeting of the Standing Committee, March 1964. 4 pts. (Reprod. from typescript). MSS. Afr. s. 1327

525. WORDSWORTH (Christopher Andrew). Political service, Nigeria: letters, 1900–06. MSS. Afr. s. 1373

SIERRA LEONE

526. BURKINSHAW (P. L.). Sierra Leone: handing-over notes, Tonkolili, Koinadugu, Bombali districts, 1953–55; Bombali district annual report, 1954. 4 pts. (Typescript). MSS. Afr. s. 1407(1)

527. *DUDLEY-NIGG (J. A.). Handing over notes as Director of Prisons, Sierra Leone, 1955. (Typescript).

528. HODGSON (Peter Charles). Miscellaneous notes on political progress in a primitive community; native courts; principles of indirect rule; Ogbeyan intelligence reports, &c., as D. O., Nigeria, 1934–44; as Commissioner, Gambia, 1944–50; Memorandum on N. J. Brooke's report on the native court system, Sierra Leone (c. 1950). MSS. Afr. s. 1215

529. SHUFFREY (Paul). Six personal letters as Administrative Officer, Sierra Leone, 1913–23, to Prof. Hale Bellot. MSS. Afr. s. 1203

530. WEIR (Neil Archibald C.). Personal diary, Nigeria, 1925–36; Sierra Leone, 1936–43; the Gambia, 1943–50, as Administrative Officer; district reports, Nigeria; Native administration notes, Sierra Leone; Lord Hailey's questionnaire, the Gambia, 1948. 9 vols. (Typescript). MSS. Afr. s. 1151

531. *———— Baoma chiefdom disturbances, Nov. 1948: report of Commission of inquiry, Oct. 1949 (N. A. C. Weir, Commissioner). (Typewritten).

532. WILLIAMS (C. V.). Reports to the Council for technical education and training for overseas countries, East Africa, May 1963; Nigeria, Sept. 1963; Sierra Leone, Nov. 1963; Draft minutes of the 8th meeting of the Standing Committee, March 1964. 4 pts. (Reprod. from typescript).   MSS. Afr. s. 1327

INDEX

(The numbers are those of the entries)